Eldoret

CULTURE AND TECHNOLOGY
Series Editor
W. David Kingery

Department of Anthropology
Department of Materials Science and Engineering
The University of Arizona

Eldoret

An African Poetics of Technology

by Richard M. Swiderski

Drawings by the Author

The University of Arizona Press

Tucson & London

The University of Arizona Press
Copyright © 1995
The Arizona Board of Regents

Printed in the United States of America

⊛ This book is printed on acid-free, archival-quality paper.

99 98 97 96 95   5 4 3 2 1

Library of Congress Cataloging-in-Publication Data

Swiderski, Richard M.
    Eldoret : an African poetics of technology / by Richard M.
Swiderski.
        p.   cm. — (Culture and technology)
    Includes bibliographical references and index.
    ISBN 0-8165-1494-1 (alk. paper)
        1. Technology—Kenya—Eldoret.   2. Technology—Social aspects—
Kenya—Eldoret.   I. Title.   II. Series.
    T28.K4E43   1995   94-27429
    306.4'6'0967627—dc20   CIP

British Cataloguing-in-Publication Data
A catalogue record for this book is available from the British Library.

to
Hans and Eunice

MZEE	NI
AJUAYE	MUNGU

THE ELDER	IS
WHO KNOWS	GOD

painted on opposite rear wheel flaps
of a minivan seen in Eldoret

The fact that all intelligent beings inhabit the same world does
not countervail against the no less momentous fact that we
inhabit very different ecological niches within it, and we bring
very different sorts of *modus operandi*—physically and cognitively as well, since we cannot separate *theoria* from *praxis*. The
chain that links cognition to power, power to a power base, and a
power base to a mode of enmeshment in nature, is wrought of
unbreakable links.

NICHOLAS RESCHER
"Extraterrestrial Science" (in Regis 1985:94)

"Hii kitu ime fail brake."

reported words of a bus driver just before an accident in which
thirteen people were killed   (*Nation,* 10 April 1993:2)

Contents

Acknowledgments ... xi

Introduction ... xiii

1. The Milkman ... 1

2. Wheeled Toys ... 17

3. The Moletrap ... 27

4. Charcoal ... 33

5. The Land ... 49

6. Inertial Balance ... 63

7. Electricity ... 79

8. The Fundi Complex ... 94

9. Teamwork and Management ... 114

10. Decisions ... 134

11. Discards ... 150

12. Fluids ... 160

13. Sign Making ... 174

14. The Empty Market ... 189

Appendix 1: Hitting Pictures ... 205

Appendix 2: Making Maps ... 209

Notes ... 211

Bibliography ... 215

Index ... 223

.

Acknowledgments

This book comes from two years spent in Africa. Any mzungu who has lasted that time owes debts to a great many people who have tolerated strange behavior and odd speech, some of it stereotypically familiar, and who have patiently given gifts which I hope show well here.

In particular I wish to thank Chief Administrative Officer Professor J. K. Sang, Professor Joshua Akong'a, Mr. Wellington Edebbe, and my other colleagues in the anthropology department at Moi University. Mr. Monsi George and his family, and Professor Hans van Doorne and his family were friends inside the hectic world of the university, and in the no less hectic world outside.

A special acknowledgment is due to Mr. Macleod and Mrs. Grace Marondo, who channeled information and ideas that might not otherwise have reached me or this book. Boys with toy cars, market women, matatu touts, hairdressers, telephone engineers, sign painters, and gardeners, among others who spoke with me and showed me their work, are mentioned in the book, by name if they so wished or did not object. There are still far too many without name, but at least not without history.

Comments by readers of the manuscript reached me in Africa soon enough to help me form the book for wider purposes. I wish especially to thank the editor of the series, Professor David Kingery, and the University of Arizona Press acquisitions editor, Dr. Christine Szuter, for their suggestions and encouragement. Only those who saw the original manuscript know how much the book owes to Ms. Alexis Mills, who edited it down to the very sentences for words and logic. In the process, she both challenged thoughtless expressions and brought out unexpressed thoughts.

My wife, Sandi Inman Swiderski, interrupted a successful career to join me in East Africa, where she had previously worked for some years. As a woman in African society, she experienced life and technology differently from me, but was willing to share her experience just the same.

Introduction

This book developed over the course of two years' residence in Eldoret, a rapidly growing town in the western highlands of Kenya. Established as a railhead on the Nairobi to Kampala line in 1923, it has become a regional market and the chief industrial town of the highlands. In the political structure of Kenya, Eldoret is a chartered municipality and the administrative center of Uasin Gishu District, which is within Rift Valley Province, headquartered in Nakuru.

My objective from the start was to observe the local operation of technology, whether peculiarly indigenous or not, in the hands and lives of the people in Eldoret. This account of my observations is divided into subjects that cut across categories of technical form to convey the centers of technological endeavor. All of the practices and people are peculiar to Eldoret in the precise historical, social, and cultural form of their operation, though any of them might be found elsewhere. I have sought to present the particulars of this African poetics of technology not by showing the different details of workmanship but by showing the cumulative quality of circumstance that amounts to a distinctive technological form.

This is both a history and an anthropology of technology. "Poetics," derived from the Greek verb *"poein"* meaning "to make or do," has as much to do with technology (material making) as with poetry (verbal making), and refers to the ongoing act of assembly that can look like the passage of time or the eternity of culture, and is actually both. It is an African poetics because the act of assembly is motivated by African conditions, and executed through the genius and strength of African people.

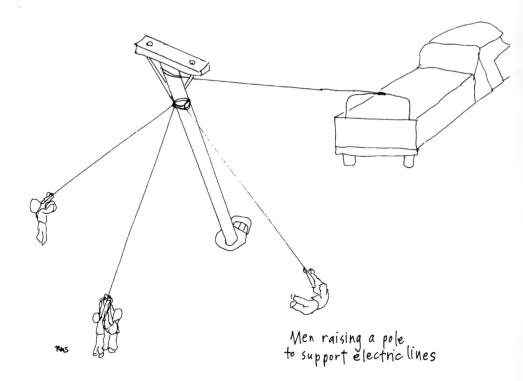

Men raising a pole
to support electric lines

One day I watched a crew of men erect a pole to string electrical wires for a newly constructed building. The pole itself was a creosote-treated tree trunk produced at the EATEC (East Africa Tannin Extract Company) plant not far away. It was tossed off a truck beside a pit in the ground, one meter deep and a half meter wide, already backed with a flat metal railroad tie. Three men tied long sisal ropes (another Kenyan product) to the pole: one length to the top and two below the cross piece.

After positioning the pole flat on the ground with the end at the pit, the rope tied to the top was taken back over the pit and tied to a horizontal bar over the rear gate of the truck. The other two ropes were drawn right and left, opposite each other and perpendicular to the top rope, with one or two men at each of these ends. The men on the rope ends then walked forward and toward the truck, pulling the bottom of the pole into the pit at an angle. While they held their ends taut, the truck began to move forward, tensing the rays of rope into a triangle and keeling the pole into the pit at an angle. The rope holders fanned back, keeping their tension, and two men standing in the back of the truck knotted the slack as the truck moved back a short distance. Then, with all lines taut, the truck moved forward again, and the end of the pole slipped into the pit, kept forward by the metal tie. The men on either side compensated for any sideways tilt, and with the ropes taut, other men advanced to steady the pole and straighten it before shoveling in dirt and compacting it to hold the pole erect. A man then shimmied up the pole and removed the tied rope ends.

The entire operation, which was repeated for eleven other poles that day, required seven men and took about fifteen minutes. The operation was a visible assembly of materials, balance, and human and mechanical strength. No one ventured near the shaft of the pole during the lift operation, yet human hands were constantly in contact with the weight of the pole. The ultimate outcome, supply of power to the building, was not directly related to the erection of the pole, but there was a relationship between the manner of erecting the pole and the technology of power supply to this particular building. An African poetics of technology describes that relationship.

Eldoret

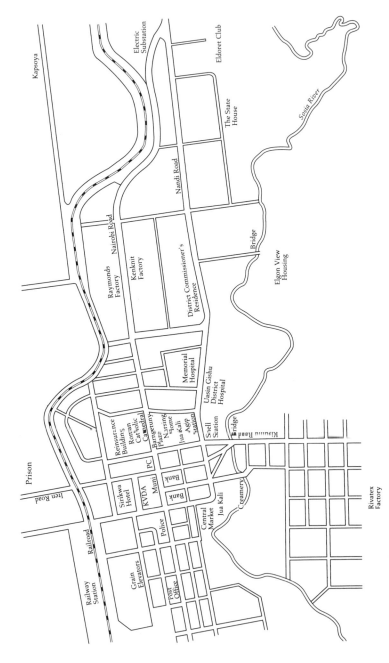

Landmarks in Eldoret, Kenya

1. The Milkman

Each morning, Kibitu the milkman rises just before dawn and with the help of his wife and two children milks their three producing cows. From the plastic receiving bucket, they pour the milk into ten-liter yellow plastic containers that originally held cooking oil. Kibitu puts about three-quarters of a liter in each and screws the cap on over a piece of plastic torn from a bag, to secure it and to keep the milk from leaking out during the ride. He places the containers in a wooden box fastened to the rear rack of his Chinese bicycle.

When he sits on the bicycle seat, his wife hands him a paper bag containing the thirty eggs collected from their free-range chickens that morning and the previous day. The eggs, too, are placed in the box behind him. Because the shells are tough from all the earth minerals in the chickens' diet, they are hard to break, so they usually survive the trip intact if Kibitu keeps the box balanced behind him.

Once properly arranged, Kibitu begins pedaling. His *shamba* (farmstead) is in Kapsoya, a sprawling collection of housing plots spread across the main highway approaching Eldoret town from the direction of Nakuru. To reach his customers, Kibitu must cross the highway and enter the area where the *wazungu*[1] dwell, which is not very far away, but he cannot take the most direct route.

To avoid being caught by the municipal workers trimming grass and clearing ditches, Kibitu follows a rutted dirt road parallel to the paved road before quickly traversing the highway and proceeding up a paved back road to the first of the six houses on his route. He must also avoid the road crews waiting while the asphalt liquifies in the drum heating over a small wood fire.

If any of the workmen recognize Kibitu, they will chase him, take away his milk, and give him a beating that could incapacitate him for days. Or they will drag him to the police station, where he will be asked if he has a license to sell raw milk, or a letter from the Ministry of Health attesting to the milk's purity. Since he cannot produce either, he would have to pay a fine equal to at least a day's earnings, and he would lose most of the morning. He would rather pay the fine occasionally and do his best to avoid capture.

Kibitu has no hope of getting a license to sell milk independently. The municipal commission expects all milk producers in Eldoret to sell directly to Kenya Cooperative Creameries, also in Kapsoya, or to Doinyo Lessos Creameries, near the Sosia River downtown. Tractors pulling carts piled with milk cans ply the roads to these places all day long.

However, Kibitu is a very small producer, and he does not like to wait months to receive payment from the creameries. He needs his daily shillings for veterinary fees, feed in spare seasons, savings for additional animals—and his bicycle. So he makes his way along the roads on a very thin edge. The wazungu and some rich Kenyans will buy from him because he comes directly to the house, and they do not need to go to the creameries or to the outdoor market and Asian-run supermarkets downtown to hunt for fresh eggs or milk.

Like other bicycle vendors, Kibitu is willing to take risks to maintain an almost self-sufficient rural existence in order to escape the impoverishing economic cycles of the city—and because that is the life they prefer. The city offers them customers and still has enough pasturage for their cows and chickens, but the city also encourages rivalries for resources.

For several days, a big black cow grazed along the road into town. To have noticed this is not a monument of anthropological observation: cows might be seen grazing along many other paths to many other cities and towns of the world. However, because the cow (literally) incorporates an ecology that developed in this area and which reflects the ecology of western Kenya, the cow is evidence that commands specific attention.

The area where the cow was grazing is a broad dirt road bordered by margins that are limited on both sides by the stone walls of house compounds. One section of the margin had been mowed, and the grass gathered into a pile and burned, but the cow did not graze the cut section. Instead, it lowered its muzzle amid the tall grass farther up the road. The cow was only in the vicinity for a few days and then vanished.

Other cows have passed down the road, briefly browsing on the margins or straying into open lots and fields before the herdsmen moved them on. The herds of fifteen to twenty animals pass along the boundary of this area, the Nairobi-Uganda highway, on their way toward new pastures. The grazing is opportunistic. Whatever the cattle eat along the way is theirs, and any greenery will be cropped until either the cows or the herdsmen decide to move elsewhere. Only the gates and the walls of the houses restrict their movement. The pasturage is permitted simply because it is taken more or less on the move.

While on a walk of my own, I followed three herdsmen along the margins of a paved main road as they headed toward town. The herdsmen kept the animals moving by walking beside them but not exerting any direct pressure. When some of the cows sauntered toward a closed metal gate, an excited dog inside caused them to bolt suddenly toward the road, but the Turkana channeled their sideward rush into the forward motion of the rest of the herd. That forward motion then had to be directed to the left, around a corner, where to continue straight would have meant blundering into the construction of new hospital buildings and the heavy traffic routed around it.

Instead, the cows turned the corner and then continued turning between two walled compounds, where they astonished an Indian woman waiting for her car. Her shout alerted the herdsman, who rapidly turned them down the slope of a rutted dirt road, over the bridge that crossed the river, and toward the pasture on the edge of a crowded housing development.

The cowherds are Turkanas,[2] but the man who owns the herd is a Somali who lives in Isiolo, some distance away. He has employed these men to manage his investment and to pasture them along the road and in what open fields they can find. They spend the night, apparently by permission, in a grassy space near the State Lodge. The Turkanas take turns minding the cattle, and the man who watches them at night milks them in the morning. He takes a five-liter container of milk to houses in the vicinity, where he has formed agreements to sell it on a regular basis. The owner of the herd sells the cows when they reach a certain size. Thus, the cows and their managers provide the little recycling possible within this space, and their movements in search of pasture mark both the interior and the borders of a particular ecology.

This herd's motion also delineated the perimeter of an area between two major paved roads: the Nairobi Road, the main thoroughfare connecting Nairobi with Kampala, Uganda, and converging into it, Nandi Road, recently paved but only intermittently open because of construction. When it is open, Nandi Road hosts an erratic concentration of vehicles—not the trucks and buses of the main road, but *matatus*, which use it as an escape route from the town. The matatus, a type of enclosed mass transport, race down the smooth paved surface of Nandi Road sometimes three abreast in the same direction, heading out toward the juncture with Nairobi Road.

Both roads bound an arc-shaped area, a niche in the city's ecology marked by the presence of a large textile factory, Ken-Knit. The factory faces Nairobi Road, with its back to the land area of the arc. Lumumba Road, broad, shaded, and paved, cuts from Nairobi Road just below the factory, straight across to Nandi Road, defining the townside chord of the arc. The area from the factory down Lumumba Road and back up Nandi Road is palisaded private property, walled or fenced private compounds, extending almost to where the roads converge and the boundaries soften (although where the roads meet, there is a new development of two-story houses, some only recently inhabited).

These public roads and the adjacent industrial and private property form what land-use specialists call a mixed or peripheral zone, an abrupt transition from open space to settled and bordered spaces. The black cow that grazed among the remaining openings of these spaces, and the herds unable to move freely through them, still find it to their advantage to pass along the routes where they are not threatened by the competition of traffic, and to pause in the spaces not yet rigidly and exclusively marked.

The cows' movements typify a passage over this land that has not yet been halted entirely but has been restricted and redefined by newly imposed boundaries. With their casual attention to an increasingly neglected resource, and their motion of pastoral foraging, the cows represent an aspect of the land's ecology in contrast with the force of travel and the absolute states of settlement and enterprise in the arc.

Boy Cowherd
demonstrating a
karate pose

The browsing of the cows contrasts not only with the rushing frenzy of vehicles but also with the purposeful walking of people along paths that admit vehicles only grudgingly, and not at the speeds of the paved roadways. One path proceeds from Nairobi Road down the center of the arc, all the way to Lumumba Road, and crosses a dirt road that connects Nairobi Road with Nandi Road above the Ken-Knit factory. Outside the factory walls, other paths parallel the dirt road and pass between Nairobi Road and Nandi Road, but these, too, are succumbing to the obstacles of enclosure and construction.

Along all of these routes, whether paved or not, moves a continual stream of people in and out of town. It might be possible to categorize them by ethnic, gender, or racial type, by language spoken, or by occupation, but the most immediate and obvious distinctions have to do with the nature of their passage. Their movements and the routes they take connect them to the other creatures within the arc, and separate them immediately from the impersonal vehicles on the boundaries.

The only vehicles that move with people are bicycles, often laden to capacity like the trucks or matatus of the roadways. The movement of bicycles is the least certain and most halting because they cannot go easily over boundaries that do not inhibit pedestrians but which motorized vehicles cannot attempt, such as the broken cement culvert that serves as a bridge over a drainage ditch. These two kinds of movement through the arc—steady, of the walkers and runners, and interrupted, of the bicycles—contrast with the uniform movement on the paved boundary roads.

On the paved roads, however, the uniformity of movement, or the speed, that wheeled vehicles can achieve is interrupted by strategically placed rows of speed bumps, which even out the differences between pedestrians and vehicles and produce a more or less uniform steady movement. The surface condition of the paths inside the arc tends toward the same steady movement by excluding cars and slowing any potentially fast vehicle like a bicycle to a walking pace. As a result, everything moving along the paths is confined to the same narrow band of speed and comes to maintain a common rhythm of a matched pace. This rhythm is always tending to be further narrowed; that is, the paths become roads traversed by traffic, which is limited in turn by the needs of pedestrians.

This tendency toward a common rhythm of travel is also encouraged by other trends in the ecology. Most noticeable are the movement variations arising from what people are carrying. Many people carry scrap wood on their heads. The wood is gathered from the remaining treed lots, or from the construction site just outside the arc, and is transported to houses further outside the town. The people forage within the arc but do not live there. However, most of what is carried along the paths has not been taken from within the arc but has been purchased in town or at one of the markets, or brought by hand through the territory because the carrier had no transportation. (Most of those who live within the arc have transportation and need no hand or head to carry essential supplies.)

The main movement of people through the arc is like the movement of cows in that they are passing through to their main activities elsewhere. This is also true of the employees and would-be employees of the textile mills along Nairobi Road. The main progress of these people is along the road to town at set times of day, but numbers of them do filter across the land by its many paths toward the factory and back again at the beginning and end of shifts.

Yet another quality of human movement is that of the *askaris*,[3] or security guards, standing watch at private houses and factories, dressed conspicuously in generic blue and red askari uniforms or those of specific security firms. Their concentration is surprisingly large, and because they often move in groups, they set a tone for the movement.

These moving populations are regular. They have goals within or through the arc, and their movements are parts of larger cycles completed with their movement through this space. Others move arbitrarily within this space or visit it without this systematic purpose.

Wanderers through the arc are defined by their contrast to those whose motion indicates purpose. They are often people taking a walk near their property, people who can afford not to have a destination. Unlike those apart from the ecology, drawing upon it and leaving through speed, these wanderers are "in" the local ecology.

The big black cow is a balance point between those two species of motion. It is a living thing at rest, yet it is also passing through, and in its grazing, the cow separates the land's product from itself. The residents who carry their children or push them in carriages demonstrate a similar stasis in motion. They resemble the wood carriers in the burdens they propel, but the different nature of the burdens distinguishes them from both the wanderers on site and those passing through.

Children themselves are another static or locally moving manifestation of the area's ecology. They might be seen wandering by themselves near the houses, possibly playing with natural products or even collecting them, but their presence seems to be compromised by the motion of those who pass through and, of course, of the vehicles. Theirs is the frailest lingering, best enclosed if it is to subsist at all. It is an index of the changing ecology of the arc that the children vanish inward or adapt. Perhaps there never was much outward child's play, and its absence is no change, but that thesis is contravened by visible changes along another path just outside the arc.

The path that connects Lumumba Road with Waigango Road is a narrow, unpaved, and rutted track between some simple one-room dwellings and a quantity of new, expensive construction on both sides. It is mainly a pedestrian route, usually fringed by children active in their games, greeting passersby and pressing out from family space. With the closure of Nandi Road, however, the hospital construction-site traffic headed out from Eldoret has begun to file along this path, and the children have disappeared. Their weak presence in other areas of the arc seems proportional to the traffic there, and presumably they have retreated to protected perimeters.

The most noticeable children (apart from those passing or being carried through) are those with distinct adaptations to vehicular motion. A few mzungu children ride through on their bicycles, their separateness made clear as much by their small recreational bicycles and their destinationless joyriding as by their appearance. Fleets of wheeled toys constitute another presence of children in this ecology. The essence of the children seems to be a *wheeled* motion.

These wheeled toys, which are not unique to this section of Eldoret, to Eldoret itself, or to Kenya, have their own place (or a motion) in the ecology. Children wheel them about singly or in groups. The arc is often visited by crowds of boys (if girls operate these toys, I have yet to see it), each with a different toy, passing through for no other purpose than running the toys down another pathway. It is a child's version of adult passage motions powered by images of vehicles they cannot yet operate.

Also passing through the arc are smoke and water, constrained by shaping influences that make them apparent evidences of the ecology. Both are year-round products of the Ken-Knit factory on the border. A plume of black smoke, as much a fixture as the area's paths and traffic, extends across the center of the arc, pouring from a tall, curving chimney. In a long-exposure photograph of moonrise, the black smoke parallels the land, even though it was not visible to the eye at the time.

Water also maintains a fluid passage through the arc. It most notably moves through deep channels (*mifereji*) dug parallel to the road. In one set of channels is a flow that is neither rain drainage nor a stream. The flow may be copious at times, less than a trickle at others, but it is always milky and unnaturally bright in color, royal purple or lime green. It is obviously an exudate of the Ken-Knit factory, flowing from an open drain beside the factory through the mifereji and away, downhill to the river, to which it imparts its colors. The water (Swahili *maji*, being a plural, is better) is like the smoke, a substance passing through the land along its own path and in the same direction, away from the factory and the road at the border. It appears that a principle of like repulsion sends it away from the road, which has its own noxious flow.

The factory faces away from the arc, but the smoke and water establish the land between the two roads as part of the factory enclosure. Despite their fluid nature, they follow rigid channels until they are expelled into the ecology of the area, of which they are characteristic components. These lasting contributions from the factory are complemented by seasonal contributions from the sky, and by the year-round burning of household trash, leaves, and cuttings.

The factory and the private residences most strongly resemble each other this way. They perpetually expel their wastes both onto the surface and through underground conduits to be transported elsewhere—most importantly, away. These expellers of waste are the only static elements on the land, and they do everything to assert their status against the movement of people and of all other things. Taking once again a broader view of the ecology, the area now appears to be a series of parallel flows, of people and fluids, all reflecting and interrupting each other, but not interacting. Passage and expulsion, rather than contact and mingling, seem to be the main characteristics. It appears to be an ecology of passages.

One passage across the land contradicts this general character, only to exemplify it. It is a paved road that crosses the tip of the arc, connecting Nairobi and Nandi Roads not far from their convergence. It is unusual in being paved, and it continues across Nandi Road to an extension, also paved. At times, the road is bordered by Kenyan flags on white poles placed at intervals along its course, which mark it as a channel for passages of national symbolic value.

Past the end of the road extension is the State Lodge, where presidential parties stay while visiting the Eldoret area. The State Lodge is the most solidly enclosed bastion in Eldoret. Though a paved road runs past it, no vehicle or pedestrian, as signs in English and Swahili announce, may pass without authorization. The remaining perimeter of the State Lodge, which overlooks a river vale and a small workers' village as well as some architecturally complex houses, is circumscribed by a chain-link fence, posted with the same signs and surveyed by guard towers. Official processions enter the grounds in complete privacy; no one else is allowed.

The State Lodge epitomizes the complete blockage of the area's natural flow, subordinated to a static enclosure that attracts a flow of its own. What is perpetual and random in the arc's flow of traffic becomes timed and ordered with reference to the State Lodge. Here the movement is only by vehicle, the slowly developing condition of motion elsewhere. Roads are paved and channels dry, walking gives way to traffic, and traffic is more and more narrowly regulated.

The internal conditions of a number of the enclosures are also like those of the State Lodge because they are establishments rather than dwellings. Some of their tenants are institutions occupying what look like houses. Other tenants are public officials whose tenancy is written all over the exterior (the District Commissioner's residence on Lumumba Road), or whose social position (Christian minister, university official) is equated with the dwelling. Many of the structures are residences by proxy, rented out by wealthy and influential absentee landlords who have built them as investments.

One property opposite the corner where Ken-Knit abuts Nairobi Road is owned by former Energy Minister Nicholas Biwott. Others are the property of an Army colonel who resides in Nairobi. The net effect is that several of these enclosures, like the State Lodge, are occupied by a political (and/or economic) presence but not inhabited by the person of that presence. Instead, a population of house servants, gardeners, maids, and askaris preserve these places primarily as enclosures, whether the person is there or not.

Many of the structures share another characteristic of the State Lodge. By default, they provide living space for some of the people moving through the area who, though they may never have title to the property and live there at the sufferance of the tenant/owner, are primary occupants. They are in residence and in transit at the same time.

The roles of these house servants and employees reflect the roles of their employers, who must be "somebody" to live there. It is likely that the servants circulate among themselves, granting to each other a freedom of movement through the well-guarded gates denied to most of the outsiders. Thus, servants speak to each other in a common language and assist each other when the need is plain. There appears to be a communal recognition of the commonalities of the place-saver role that eases divisions between ethnic and religious groups. The context of servitude or of house-guarding/maintenance is a medium through which Luhya permits Kikuyu passage because both are maids. It is not clear, however, how far these passages subvert the preponderant restriction of flow, and thus contribute to the ecology of the area.

One dwelling is different from the rest. Unenclosed and unguarded, not subordinate to an enclosure, it is a small concrete block set amid its own cornfield. Although visible from the central path, it is not on any path or road. There are no gates or outbuildings, and no signs of habitation other than smoke from the chimney and a regular Sunday evening open fire in the yard. The building is such a departure from the arc's standards—so permeable—that it is the subject of local folklore. It is said that the inhabitant of the house is an elderly woman immobilized by a long illness and cared for by a Kenyan retainer entirely devoted to her. The retainer has long since ceased to receive any remuneration and has instead begun to use his own savings to supply her wants.

The story stresses a static point in the ecology, where a white, most often the inhabitant of an enclosure, exists in a wholly dependent relationship with a "native," who maintains the flow into her unguarded house. This is the same as the model provided by the State Lodge except that it reveals an interior actually tended by local people while the pretense of residence is reduced to a single surviving mzungu.

In this exposed dwelling, the pattern of the ecology returns to the terms of the big black cow, who, like the mzungu in the solitary house, subsists upon the land through the means of a keeper. The cow is kept on the margin, excluded from enclosed compounds that interrupt and channel the flow through the area. There is every sign that the private compounds will continue to enclose the space and further differentiate it from public channels and private residences. The cow will then either be a part of the flow outside, no longer able to pause in its ambiguous status, or it will exist inside an enclosure as another piece of private property. Most likely it will not be there at all, having lost its platform in the ecology of a temporary stasis or a slow movement.

Some animals still live in the wild of the arc, and not just the invisible hordes of insects that attract attention only when they interfere with some human activity (for example, the mosquitoes that breed in the long grass providing a reason to permit the cow's trimming activities). Birds and lizards pass inviolate between the public and private domains, participating in an ecology that has become almost irrelevant to the arc, although it still accounts for the bulk of the biomass. Occasionally, a chameleon is visible crossing a road or a garden, the color changes and shaking motion that make it impossible to detect in vegetation making it comically conspicuous on the soil, and already vulnerable to predators and passing traffic.

An overview of the area's ecology shows how this creature's inappropriateness to the area's present ecology leads to its destruction—not through general forces of change, but through shifts in land use and the human presence. Unlike the humans, the chameleon has not adapted by specializing in house service to win a place and a right to transit.

A larger animal that has demonstrated a fit into the ecology is the hadada ibis, a large bird with small head, curved bill, and a distinctive trumpet call. The ibises are attracted to human refuse and the pickings of mowed and cleared land, and they are not averse to perching on houses or nesting in their vicinity. Yet the ibises, too, require a share of the land. Thus, the future of these travelers with a commonly denied freedom, who preserve an essence apart from the arc's state and trend, is in doubt, but their cries are a reminder that there is an alternative to walls and traffic.

This is an ecology of passages and of relations in movement. Figures in this space approach each other, make contact, and then move on to other purposes outside. Those with more opportunities for contact seem to have a degree of residence in the space, a more ramified if not deeper participation in the ecology. Their presence begins to resemble something social, which can be seen as lapsed or restricted motion, but is still fundamentally motion through the arc.

Men, women, and children often walk along Nandi Road in groups, pausing to talk before continuing on their way. Some wear uniforms and have clear destinations and purposes in their travel. The only large aggregations are near the factory or the primary school, as if the permanent status of those institutions allows more of a social formation, but only to the extent that the timing and functions of those institutions allow. The State Lodge, however, is the exception that sets the standard for the entire area.

On many Sunday mornings, men wearing clean suit jackets and possibly ties gather near the posted turnoff to the Eldoret Club. They stand in clusters on the shoulder where the matatus from town discharge their passengers, on the grassy area near the sign and along the unpaved road leading to the club. The groups can grow rather large, some arriving together in vehicles hired for that purpose, and they speak among themselves enthusiastically. Occasionally, a formally dressed woman joins the group. The separate bodies, linked by conversations between the boundary members, can extend along the road and onto a paved drive leading to some houses. Here a cluster can form around some individual who clearly commands attention. A gathering this large and fixed in a place where only a few people may normally stand waiting for transport must be a full stop in the flow of the area. The fullest stop is the State Lodge, associated with political power; the others are official residences and walled compounds, associated with political or economic power.

One Sunday, walking up Nandi Road with a copy of the newspaper in my pack, I approached a group of men in suits also making their way up the road, talking among themselves in Kalenjin. One of the men detached himself from the group and exchanged greetings with me in English. He asked where I was going, and I answered noncommittally, gesturing in the direction of the club. He nodded his head and, smiling, said, "Ah, to see our friend." I continued as he turned aside to join the other men who had crossed to join those at the matatu stop. Asking the others spread along the road, I found that they were waiting for a prominent local politician who hosts Sunday gatherings at the club.

This man is a member of parliament, and Eldoret is the largest city near his district. He arrives driving his own vehicle, not being accorded the presidential prestige of a State Lodge venue for his meetings, but he turns the club and the road leading to it into a temporary, scaled-down State Lodge through the waiting his visits inspire. The politician and his visitors are just passing through, their niche in the ecology being that of high society.

Across the arc, near the border with Nairobi Road, are three houses owned by a military figure, two tenanted by Moi University faculty members, and one by a bank manager. All these houses are served by domestic and yard staff.

A man named Yusup was employed as a gardener by the two faculty members, and he worked there for some time before leaving one for not paying his wages, and then the other in the aftermath of a quarrel. He was a Bukusu[4] from the vicinity of Lugulu, and he had come to work in Eldoret after being forced to leave home by his father's new wife. A woman from his village who was a maid in one of the houses had found him the position. Yusup, his wife, and their young child shared with another family a single room in a housing tract on the distant side of Eldoret.

Yusup walked the seven kilometers to work every day, arriving by 8:00 A.M. His monthly salary for both jobs totaled 650 Kenyan shillings. He was required to cut the grass, weed the plantings, plant and cultivate a vegetable garden, and tend two sheep. He dug trenches to capture moles that attacked the gardens, and he periodically burned the trash in an open field behind the house. He never missed a day's work, even when noticeably ill. But when he heaped soil near the driveway in the course of digging a pit to plant some trees, his employer castigated him, and he defended himself, finally quitting in the ensuing wrangle. Lacking a recommendation from his irate employer, Yusup sought help from others who knew him and was able to get some work on road crews. He considered moving with his wife and child back to his homeland.

Yusup had passed through the arc at one end of a loop, the farthest he had ventured from his place of birth. He fit into the ecology working in the soil as he had always done, but the fact that the condition of the soil is judged by others meant he could not stay there on those terms.

The ecology of the arc, besides being one of passages, seems also to emphasize a mediated relationship between people and the land. There is no need to consider who is "native" and who foreign, since those who control resources can exercise command over the allocation of space. The powerful politician and the gardener are equally foreigners, and they have the ability to legitimize the access of other foreigners by exercising influence or by digging gardens. The arc is an area of superficial exchanges, but those fleeting contacts embody larger issues of power and subsistence in the immediate attributes of the land.

One day in mid-February, a large logging truck emerged from a driveway on Nandi Road heavily loaded with split blue-gum wood. It turned toward town and lumbered for about fifty yards before the rear axle cracked, and the vehicle tilted left into the pavement and halted. The driver stacked pieces of wood beneath the chassis to keep it from capsizing. The driver's assistant remained with the stricken truck during the next few days as the wood was slowly unloaded and carried off by cyclists, convoys of them riding in rows down the road. Once emptied of its load, the truck was jacked up, and the axle removed and examined by a mechanic from town. He replaced the stripped gear and restored the axle well enough to make the truck roadworthy. The driver reappeared to drive it to the truck repair yard downtown. All that remained of the mishap were oil smears and some indentations in the recently paved surface of Nandi Road. Kibitu the milkman told me about it when he came the following morning. Even the trees had become part of the flow of movement through the arc.

2. Wheeled Toys

On a street of very heavy traffic between Nairobi and the west of Kenya, I came face to face with a young man. What caught my attention first was his dress. His clothes were exploded in tatters at the knees and elbows, which were visibly thin. He stood very still as everyone else passed, and I noticed he was holding a stiff black wire bent into a series of ripples that angled sharply into the hollow core of an automobile oil filter. Festooning him were long black rubber strands dangling from the wire piece over his wrist. I had at first mistaken them for other remnants of his clothes. We continued looking at each other, each making his assessment, paused in a motor career that urged us to continue. There was nothing to say, so I walked on without saying anything.

Afterwards, I began to place the boy within the schemata I use to identify people. He was not in school: he had no uniform, and it was school time when I saw him. He seemed to be of school age, but he was malnourished, so there was no telling his age outside a broad range. There was no sign of what he was doing or where he was going, except for that piece of trash at the end of the wire. I decided that this was a toy, or the remains of one, or an attempt to make one.

During the dry season, and especially around Christmastime, boys are often seen pushing wheeled toys through the streets. These toys are made from found materials, wood or wire, shaped into open frames resembling cars and trucks, and adorned with milk containers or bright red batteries that also provide inertial balance. Although they differ greatly from each other in execution, the toys are consistent in form. Using a long stiff wire attached to one of the axles, the boys push the toys along the streets, by themselves or sometimes in groups, ranging a distance from their homes. Unlike skateboards and other more costly manufactured devices run by children elsewhere, the wheeled toys never appear on crowded streets. They are more likely to be run on the shoulder of the highway, where a boy can pause beside a parked long-haul tandem trailer and maybe exchange a few words with the driver.

Although some boys make full-bodied car or truck toys, many toys are just a single axle with wheels, or a lone wheel at the end of a pole, perhaps decorated with a carton or a plastic bottle. The pole can be a modest shaft or a massive pole with protruding horizontal steering bars that translate some of the motion of a tiny wheel into a grander sweep. Eldoret boys running their wheels over the land look like Indian village children doing the same (photo in Smithsonian 1985:215), and they are also like the Malagasy boys, who use their handmade wooden vehicles for transport or to carry smaller children about the village (Mack 1986:16).

The wheeled toys can be made of original materials, most often of wooden blocks shaped to form chassis, wheels, and pole, but often they are units of recycling. For many children, the manufacture of wheeled toys is their first experience separating materials from their usual uses. The wheels are taken from other toys, or are simply plastic lids, the rims of metal cans, or loops of stiff wire—anything circular that can turn on an axle. The wheels might be paired and joined with an axle, and tightly wrapped with paper and plastic for a smoother run.

Children also run hoops with sticks, like illustrations from early-twentieth-century children's books or one old Massachusetts traffic sign ("Children at Play") I have seen. Thin bicycle tires can be run with a piece of wire, bent at the tip, that fits into the tube slot. A child can then drive the wheel by holding the wire stationary while running alongside the rolling tire. Another method involves looping twine around the cross-section of the tire and attaching a stick to guide it. The boy I encountered was probably trying to use the wire to run his oil filter on the ground. The rubber strips were probably cut from a tire inner tube, the strands of which are commonly used to wrap everything from wounded fingers to leaky water pipes.

Boys also run useless automobile tires, and in this they resemble adult men on the streets of Eldoret, bringing tires from one place to another—two or three at a time, gigantic tractor tires and small cart tires—by hand-rolling them. There used to be a large tire dump at one corner of the Eldoret outdoor market where young men lingered, serving as tire deliverers and learning the techniques of tire removal, leak detection, seating, and inflation. This operation vanished when the municipality wiped out that section in early 1993, but its functions were distributed to outdoor automotive shops and spare parts shops.

The boy I encountered was trying to be part of this system, aspiring to the same group play of other children. But the boy, probably abandoned by his parents or left to roam, was alone, and his toy, constructed from discards, was not like anyone else's. The boy is to other boys as his toy is to their toys. Still, it was a toy, and culturally about technology, as toys often are.

I once watched three boys remove long fluorescent tubes from a dustbin outside a hardware store and bring them down to the grassy slope in front of the post office, where they staged a sword battle. At first, they delicately resisted making contact. Then, with a sudden flash, they struck them against each other, continuing until the jagged metal-pronged caps were all that remained in their hands.

Most of the men seem to go through life carrying functional and symbolic sticks. Sometimes boys and men, even in the city, can be seen carrying switches they have cut from trees (which may be from acacia saplings or from the "toothbrush tree" [*mswaki*]) to herd animals or to brush teeth. Chiefs, elders, and the president of the republic carry *rungu*, knobbed staffs of office. Men sometimes carry lengths of ten-gauge steel wire with a loop at one end, a herdsman's device used to snag the horn of an unruly cow. Herdsmen drive their cows within the precincts of the city, keeping them in line and away from traffic with a skillful javelin toss toward the cow's nose.

Another boy, also in ragged clothes and not in school, made what he called a "Mercedes," a car-shaped frame formed of lengths of wire extracted from tires and wrapped together to form a beautiful piece about one-half meter long, with a little steering wheel, a wire bent to represent a rear-view mirror, and extending antennas. The long wire handling shaft was attached from above to a piece extending the length of the car body and pivoted there to a length of wire almost spanning the width of the car. At each end of this wire, tiny wire cages filled with tufts of felt batting rotated freely with motion—the wheels. By twisting the handling shaft right or left, the operator could make the front wheel assembly turn in either direction. The rear wheels turned on a fixed crossbar. The whole is a projection of the same motion gained from a single wheel or oil filter at the end of a rod. It is a matter of individual temperament and the kinds of materials available. The boy who made the Mercedes wrapped the wires of his frame with the same strands of rubber from auto tires that festooned the street boy.

Wherever possible, a piece of a real car is incorporated into the toy. Auto oil filters are reused until they degenerate beyond restoration. The blackened, fan-folded paper cores are spread on the ground to drain and then are refitted into the metal canister for more service. When finally spent, the whole filters are tossed aside in auto yards and on river banks. Children can pick them up and make them the wheels of their devices because no one will contest their right to something so utterly discarded. The toys are at the base level of a tall pyramid of recycling. They incorporate materials exhausted beyond adult reuse. This refuse takes the shape of wheeled vehicles because of who has access to it and how they obtain it.

The power source of the toys is also scrap. Sometimes a real, but defunct, power source is used. Bright red Eveready batteries, manufactured by a Kenyan firm in Nakuru, can be secured to the inside of the frame, which might also have a spark plug or a rotor entwined in the wires.

The downtown supermarkets sell molded plastic cars with windup friction motors. Inside the glass display cases are even radio-controlled devices. These are not seen on the street, but can be glimpsed inside the compounds of Asian families. The handmade street toys are not bought and are not for sale. The children who construct them exercise a generally tool-less craftsmanship of twisting and bending wire, and wrapping rubber strips. They often work in groups, helping and influencing each other, or getting help from an older boy or parent who passes down the shape and technique. (Although these adult males clearly recall their own ventures into making toys, they do not make toys even for their own children.)

Often there are schools or teams of car runners around the same age with vehicles that resemble each other. In the large worker settlements (Langas, Huruma) outside Eldoret,[1] it is even possible to come across a wheeled-toy factory where boys have gathered the materials and are experimenting with teamwork and management in putting them together. The desire to have a model that is better and looks different is in equilibrium with the wish to have one that belongs with the others. The cars in a group are not identical, not because they cannot be, but because of these opposing intents in their design. A boy will rarely settle for a wheeled stick when others have cars, but if he must, it will be a massive, splendidly decorated stick with an unusual, colored wheel or hoop he runs through the streets.

I encountered one boy seated with his car at his side on the corner of a road, and I asked him if I could photograph the vehicle, which he called simply *gari*, the same as an automobile. He agreed, but he understood my Kiswahili request to include a photo of him with the car, and of his younger brother with him. After I had taken the photo, he told me to wait and he would see if a friend with a *basi* was around. He couldn't find him then, but later in the day, walking up the same road, I found him running his car along with another boy who had a larger model (a "bus") of comparable design. They also agreed to a photograph, in exchange for the promise of a print.

These two toys (though the boys would not accept the word *mchezi*, "plaything or game," for either) came from the same workshop, conducted by the elder boy Isaac who had made the bus. Isaac showed a proprietary overseership of both toys, pointing out the finer features and pausing to straighten a bent wheel with his fingers. Both models were formed of stiff wire crisscrossed by strands of more supple wire to form a surface. The wire, they said, was obtained from hardware stores that sell off surplus from the ends of reels and from telephone crewmen.

Some of the wires were covered with colorful insulation, and others were bare and bent in curved patterns. In the mesh of wire was a variety of plastic objects, pieces of paper with printing, and metal foil. All of the

Boy with a wheeled toy (basi)

components were manufactured; there was not a single plant or animal specimen, not even a piece of carved wood. The action of both cars was the drive rod attached to a front axle suspending cotton-bast cushioned wire wheels, and pivoting on the frame. A wire steering wheel was at the head of each rod, which inclined against the frame when not in use.

While the appearance and resemblances of the cars were important to the boys, they placed equal emphasis on the suspension, the manner in which the wheels are carried over the terrain while held on the axle in the frame. The body and decorations are for looking, but the wheels are for action.

"Action" is a label for the mechanized drive of movies that many boys, and more adult men, like to watch, and for the spirit of the annual Safari Rally. In a gari, "action" means the ability to move quickly over rugged roads and through mud without breaking down. The boys believe the action lies in the design and execution of the suspension, and they are forever checking, refitting, and modifying the axle's relationship to the frame and wheels. When they hold a rally of their own, in which boys push their own cars over a set route, the winner's suspension is carefully inspected and copied. The relative size and strength of the boy himself is not an explanation.

Two weeks later, I found the same two boys in the same place but with different cars. The younger brother, who did not have a car before, now pushed a simple wire frame "Peugeot." The older brother had reworked his car into a lower-built model with the colored inserts clustered at the front. The alterations, he said, made his car "faster" and were modeled after a Safari Rally racing car he had seen.

The rally itself had been months earlier, and all the contestants had driven through Eldoret on the Friday before Easter, which is an official holiday. The racing car did not develop until the boy had already made his model and could modify that base to suit his aspirations, while helping his brother make one of his own. He had changed the suspension from an attachment with loops of string to one with loops of insulated wire, which he said let the axle turn without catching. The boys, Turkana migrants from the north who had had some primary schooling, often lingered at the street corner where I first saw them, but eventually they found employment herding some cows that were grazed at roadside. They never ran their cars again that I saw them.

The pattern of the cars is fixed by these forces: the materials, tradition, innovation, conformity, competition, perception of the object represented, and its role in the representers' view of the world. The car is most

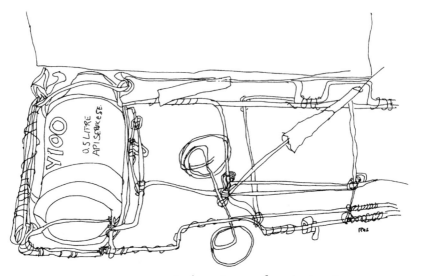

Power plant and drive train of a wheeled toy

basically a round object capable of turning beneath an open lined frame. In three dimensions, it is a persistent oblong shape with a marked front, and wheels visible through the frame. In two-dimensional representations, it is a box with the headlights turned into the viewer's field of vision, and two, three, or four circles positioned to represent wheels.

The same three-dimensional car is found all over Kenya. Toy cars made of earth or clay in the collections of the national museums in Kisumu and Nairobi are the frame model filled in with a solid substance. A "Kenyan toy car" in the collection of the Museum of International Folk Art in Santa Fe, New Mexico, is very like the Mercedes described above and similar to toy cars observed from Isiolo to Mombasa. The two-dimensional figures reflect the same consistency of design. A remarkable set of drawings scratched in a plaster wall at about one meter above ground level along a back street in Eldoret show "Volkswagen," "Peugeot," and "Mercedes" figures that closely resemble drawings derived from children's art used to decorate a card published by the Watatu Gallery, Nairobi. This is a recognized "boys'" device in a Kenyan design stream in active transmission (remembered and passed on by adults), and like more figures and ideas than its community is likely to admit, this design does not obey ethnic or "tribal" boundaries.

The design may correspond to class boundaries. The street boy I encountered was a scavenger who obtains his livelihood by gleaning the dumpsters in the market and elsewhere about town. Now that centralized trash collection has been established in Eldoret, an efficient truck makes weekly rounds, emptying each dumpster (which on one or two occasions contained a sleeping child) into its back. The children work silently inside the container, carefully sorting through the accumulated refuse looking for paper and other materials to sell, or simply food to eat. They pass through the city carrying grain bags to hold their gatherings, and they follow a route from one location to another searching for food and bottles. (The aluminum cans that are good scavenger fare in the industrial democracies are not found because they are an expensive import—five times the bottle price—and their purchasers don't surrender them.)

There also are adult scavengers, and in Eldoret, several families are almost caste-like in its practice. The streets of Eldoret are not littered by anything that can be eaten, used, or sold, and this cleanliness is not due to the municipal trash collection service.

Whether the scavenger children can assemble magnificent toys from their findings is unclear. They may not have the free time or energy. The boy I encountered seems to have gone as far as possible bringing together what he could hold, in the time he could manage, under the guidance provided by parental transmission and play association with other boys. His scavenging was vocational and did not admit play, yet he mimicked the form with the materials at hand.

Admittedly, one sighting of a form is a poor basis for generalizations about technology. The patterns that surround this attempt at a wheeled toy, the spent oil filter dangling on a wire tangled with rubber bands, order themselves socially and economically. However, as an imitation of an imitation of technology, this unique wheeled toy sketches an ecology not altogether logical or consistent, and it introduces some of the terms under which different people use, produce, and crave technology in Eldoret.

The wheeled toys, like cows, chickens, and milkmen, are found throughout the Eldoret landscape, urban and rural. The toys are a technology for experiencing the land that resists separating urban from rural. They are the boys' attempt to join the motion that links town and country, through the image of the automotive technology that does just that. But wheeled toys have social implications not inherent in the technology they mimic. Ingeniously formed with modest materials, the toys allow young men a motion they hope some day to realize more fully.

3. The Mole Trap

The mole is one wild animal that persists even as the land is given over to domestic animals, houses, and roadways. Their courses appear on the ground during the dry season as they range beneath the surface seeking the most succulent roots. Moles are especially attracted to lawns and gardens where watering has stimulated growth, and where gardeners plant vegetables that form thick root systems.

Even in its outer reaches, Eldoret has an underground of water pipes and sewage outlets that may leak and foster growth interesting to moles. This intricate and contested network of water, sewer, electrical, and telephone lines is ever changing under the supervision of authorities not in direct communication with each other, and the soil in these places is often broken, loose, and easy to tunnel. Although the moles are not as numerous as the black rats and various mice that surround human sites, human habitation invites their presence.

Moles are not usually hunted in the wild, but their depredations upon gardens often cause concern. The prospect of employment on large estates with lawns and other plantings made being able to eliminate the creatures an advantage. Still, the right technology did not develop immediately.

Wanyonyi was a Luhya boy from Kakamega who had spent his childhood herding cows, but through the agency of a kinswoman, he found employment as a gardener in the compound of an Asian family in Eldoret. Lacking experience and unable to speak even Swahili very well, he did not ask the wages of the Kikuyu gardeners. He was strong and diligent, and using only a *jembe*, a shovel at a right angle to the handle, he dug out flower beds and then planted the seedlings his employers had started.

He also began a small vegetable garden. Of those he cultivated, he recognized only maize and potatoes. Others were new to him, but he made them grow as well. When he was asked to tend a pair of sheep—adopted to serve as lawn mowers and a source of meat—he was more attuned to the task. Each day he walked to the compound from the room he shared with three other men in Kapsoya, let the sheep out of their pen and tethered them, and began his gardening. One morning, the elderly mistress of the house pointed out the line of a mole's digging aimed toward a bed of exotic bamboo, and she made it known that he must devote himself to capturing the animal.

Wanyonyi reasoned that the mole, being underground, was best captured by digging. He had never seen a mole and did not know how it moved or what it did, other than that it was a threat to the cultivated plants. He used his jembe to dig a trench where the trail approached the bamboo, down to where he found the mole's tunnel. Noting that the tunnel continued toward the plants, he followed it, but to his surprise, there was no mole where the tunnel petered out. He turned around and followed the tunnel backward along the trail, determinedly digging out over a meter of the lawn. Still no mole.

The soil became crumbly, and it was difficult to determine where the tunnel continued. Wanyonyi brought the garden hose to the trench and forced water into the tunnel, assuming the mole would be drowned. This was based on his observation that the floor of the mole's tunnel was compacted and hard, hence it might carry water like the hose itself. At that moment, Mrs. Bhalla saw what he was doing from an upper-story window, and came out of the house shouting at him in Hindi. (Kenyan "Asians," of Indian origin, can only be sure that they share Hindi and English with each other. Since many Kenyans speak English, an Asian who wants to be heard and understood by other Asians, but not by a Kenyan, will probably use Hindi.) She then told Wanyonyi in Swahili that he had ruined the lawn, and that he should leave immediately and never return.

The mole proved to be the point at which Wanyonyi's adaptability broke down. He had assumed that gardening problems could be solved with gardening techniques.

The Eldoret Club, with a membership almost entirely Asian and Euro-American (including South African), is a holdover colonial institution connected with similar clubs in Kenya, Tanzania, and Uganda. Kenyan askaris prevent nonmembers (generally Kenyans) from entering the premises, but the club regularly employs Simon, a man who works as a gardener at one of the houses in the vicinity, to catch the moles that infest the golf course.

The moles are capable of throwing heaps of reddish soil onto the seasonal green of the fairway, and the club is eager to spare its members the sight. Instead of digging unsightly trenches in the vicinity of the mole's activity, the manager employs Simon to set snares.

Simon has adapted the spring snare of small-game hunting to the underground of moles. He cuts a sapling, plants it firmly in the ground at one end, and digging a small hole, secures the other end to a stake at the side of the hole with some tight bands of bark. The sapling forms an arc with its end held in the hole under tension. Above the end of the sapling, Simon ties a thin wire that ends in a slip-knotted loop. He positions the loop before the bands that secure the end of the sapling, and being careful not to disturb the position of the loop, he covers the hole with dirt. The next morning, the mole is hanging from the sapling, strangled by the wire loop around his throat.

The design of this spring snare, most often set above ground, is common throughout the world, and the Polynesian islanders on Kiribati use a similar principle to catch rats troubling their plantings (Koch 1986: 112). Whether this trap spread from a central place or evolved independently, an ingenious individual could have crafted it wherever materials and need called for such a construction.

For the gardeners on the Eldoret periphery, the moletrap, traditional or not, is an alternative to the chemical poisons that they believe poison not only the mole but also the ground and the plants growing there.

Cross-section of ground with a moletrap

Although the gardeners speak of herbs that can be left in a tunnel to poison a mole "naturally," they do not want to risk the mole's outguessing them. The snare is the preferred design.

Simon knows that a mole will tunnel through the loop with enough force to spring the snare and that it will eat through the bands securing the end of the spring—and even be attracted to the task. He also knows precisely to what depth he must dig the hole and how far the loop must be from the stake and bands for the snare to work. It is a machine with the mole as its drive shaft, engineered psychologically to carry the motion to completion.

Simon is not the only one who has adapted a hunter's technology and understanding of animal behavior to the task of keeping a golf course (and gardens) clear of moles. He has a competitor in Peter, another local gardener. Peter makes snares of similar design, but he uses an aromatic plant as bait. The two men hire themselves out to other gardeners in the area for a flat ten-shilling fee per mole exhibited, and seldom does a sapling rise without a mole's body.

Simon and Peter, Kikuyu natives of Central Province in Kenya, are heirs to a hunting technology that was adapted long ago to solve pest-control problems on the estates where their forebears were employed. Their methods of mole capture made their way to Eldoret borne by the people who migrated there for economic reasons, and the technology continues to develop as other gardeners copy it on a trial-and-error basis. The mistake of digging trenches and the danger of using poisons are equally clear to them. The trap will persist as long as the delicate stream of its transmission is sustained by need—and the lack of a less expensive method. The mole traps will be needed as long as there is a golf course, and even more as the houses and gardens of the affluent who patronize the golf course fill the outskirts of town and create fertile ground for moles.

Mark, a gardener at a house near the golf course, learned the mole-trapping technique from Peter and added some refinements of his own. The garden is a game against nature, and the mole is one of nature's champions, better defeated by guile than by digging, which the close-planted garden cannot afford. Mole damage is especially visible when bright green leaves suddenly turn brown, and Mark noticed that a mole had been ruining recently transplanted leaf greens. He made a small hole near a browning cluster, and deeper down than usual, he found the mole's chamber with three tunnels branching out in different directions. The mole, he said, was sure to return after the ground was closed again because the creature would not dig new "roads" (*njia*) if he had already established some at this depth. Mark set a snare at the juncture of the three roads.

It took him about ten minutes to complete the operation. First he looped wire to form a slipknot snare and placed it inside an intact section of tunnel, with the free end of the wire extending aboveground. He then shaped a peg from a piece of wood and tied one end of a short piece of twine to the peg before driving it deep into the ground at the base of the tunnel that he thought the mole would most likely use to reenter the garden. Indeed, he conceived of the mole's behavior in terms of motion along this one tunnel toward the roots of the garden. The mole would find the other tunnels "cold" (without tempting scents) and try the snared one.

Skillfully avoiding the leaf plants in growth, Mark planted one end of a long, pliant blue-gum stick deep in the soil beyond the edge of the garden. The other end he arched over to the excavation. He fastened the end of the staked twine to the stick so that it crossed the front of the exposed hole and kept the stick arched at uniform tension. He attached the free end of the wire snare to the stick a short way from the twine. The snare was set, but he didn't bury the excavated chamber. Instead, he plucked and rubbed some marigold greens and placed them in the bottom of the pit. He then set some short sticks over the top by way of shoring, and roofed it with a few more leaves and a light layer of soil. Although the plants would attract the mole, who would eat through the twine to get to them, he would not proceed if he sensed light. It did not take long for the mole to do as predicted, and one more threat to the garden was removed.

The moletrap is one part of a technology complex that has enabled this dependent population of migrants to adapt to the city. Although they were herdsmen, hunters, and farmers, now they serve as gardeners and watchmen. They do not have to face animals as destructive as elephants and baboons, as some farmers in Kenya still must, but their efforts must be finely adjusted to straitened resources and the demands of employers and property owners.

4. Charcoal

Warmth and cooking heat are basic needs of the people who live in El-doret. In general, heat is provided by charcoal, natural gas, kerosene (called "paraffin" in Kenya), or electricity. However, charcoal (*makaa*)[1] is by far the favorite source of heat, and one that in itself requires a technology.

The relative use of heat sources follows an economic gradient. Electricity, the most expensive, requires imported equipment because Kenya does not have an electrical appliance industry. Stoves, heaters, and the like are still uncommon outside of cities. Gas requires simpler equipment and is supplied from a tank that is at least movable, if not portable. (Much-battered gas cylinders are another species of objects rolled through the streets.) Gas also is less costly than electricity because its siting does not have to be figured into the cost of its use.

Charcoal is the most widely used fuel because its raw materials are, for the most part, readily available, and the equipment is minimal and need not be fixed in any one location (although this is becoming controversial). Charcoal is also light; a comparable gas source of heat in BTUS would probably weigh much less than charcoal, but the vessel required by gas makes up the difference. Charcoal is available commercially in large sacks transported by bicycle and motor vehicle, and black crumbs lying on the roadside show where a sack has fallen. Women collect these charcoal "fines" and mix them with earth to make fire bricks.

The production of charcoal is usually collective, seldom individual. A small piece of land must be completely dedicated to charcoal production. Transporting the wood, preparing it, and monitoring the burning are not solitary tasks. The important difference between this heat-supplying technology and the others is that with charcoal, labor can be substituted for monetary outlay and equipment, in other words, for capital (Foley 1986:18).

There are no hereditary or occupational charcoal makers in Eldoret as there are or have been in other places (including England). People make charcoal for themselves and sell the surplus. Some may collect and broker quantities of charcoal, taking responsibility for transporting it, but fluctuating supplies of trees and opportunities (*because* it is not occupational) make such entrepreneurship provisional. People make charcoal when they have the wood and the land to site the kiln. There is always a need.

The East Africa Tannin Extract Company (EATEC, a branch of the South African conglomerate LONRHO) has extensive wattle plantations on the outskirts of town. The company was formed in the 1930s by South Africans who migrated into Eldoret and established EATEC as the first large-scale commercial operation in the area. The bark of the wattles is rendered into tannin, and the trunks are either chemically treated for use as utility poles or converted into charcoal in the company's fourteen beehive ovens. It is the only commercial charcoal-making operation in Kenya (Hankins 1987:53). EATEC's charcoal is sold in town and exported to other parts of Kenya. Conversion of wood into charcoal makes long-distance shipment of fuel wood more economical.

Charcoal for domestic use in Eldoret is also produced on a small scale locally. When possible, Mark and Muindi often cooperated in making charcoal. Mark is a gardener resident with his wife and child at a large house on the outskirts of Eldoret town. Muindi is the gardener for the house next door. Both maintain lawns and large, productive gardens in the rough area across from the houses.

Because they could not find work near their rural homes, Mark and Muindi brought their farming skills to the urban proximity, where they sought work as gardeners. Mark attended secondary school before the initiation of school fees in 1976 caused him to halt his formal education and look for a job. Instead of attending school part-time while working, and possibly waiting until his twenties to receive his diploma, Mark obtained a driver's license (no inexpensive procedure in itself), found a gardening position that included housing, married, and gained what skills came his way. (However, when the family for whom he was gardener left, he had to return to his home area.)

For charcoal users, the landscape is a "fuelscape" with a complex economics of gathering, replacement, and substitution of resources (Wisner 1989:186, 244). Mark and Muindi gathered wood nearby where continuing deforestation provided a small supply. When three large blue gums (a fast-growing variety of eucalyptus brought from Australia) were taken down by panga and handsaw in the lot across the main paved road, Muindi secured a number of logs and some branches from the project. This small supply of wood and the chance to use the space was one occasion for making charcoal.

The place where they made the charcoal was a clearing where people used to burn trash. First the men trimmed the logs and stripped their thick bark with a small hand ax. They spread some small pieces of wood and chips to form the floor of the charcoal kiln, and then they piled the logs horizontally in an open pyramid with sheets of bark, tufts of dried grass, and loosely placed branches in the openings. Then they mounded soil over this pile, about five centimeters thick, but not so much to fill in the open spaces. The mound was small by general charcoal-making standards, about one meter wide, two meters long, and one meter high—for a total volume of two cubic meters. An opening was left at one end of the mound, in which they placed a tuft of grass.

If the wood is properly dry, and the logs rest close enough to each other but not too close inside the mound, it will not take much to ignite it by placing fire at the opening. The wood will burn slowly for several days with a fire that evacuates it of water and induces combustion (pyrolysis) while leaving the shape of the branches intact. The charcoal maker says in Kikuyu that it "keeps its shape." If rain falls or a strong wind blows, the soil keeps the logs from being reduced to ash or from failing to carbonize all the way through by regulating the supply of oxygen over the entire surface and holding the heat within the mound. If the earth covering becomes dry and crumbles away, it loses its capacity to regulate the burning, so the men see to it that the mound is watered evenly at intervals. The result is a steady release of white smoke that is mostly steam, which tells them the burning is proceeding as it should.

Mark and Muindi know how to space the logs, what size logs to use, when to remove the bark (and when not to), what kinds of wood burn together, and when wood is too dry to use for charcoal making. Charcoal making in itself does not provide them with primary benefits: they cannot warm themselves or cook their food by the charcoal-making fire because it is too slow, too smokey, and too far from their dwellings.

Making charcoal is a technology of energy conservation and control. From what is known of how wood becomes charcoal in an earth kiln (Foley 1986:64–68), Mark and Muindi's procedure is one of the simplest ways to control the phases of drying, pyrolysis, and cooling that yield usable charcoal. Yet even though their technology is not governed by a scientific (i.e., experimentally measured) understanding of the difference between endothermic and exothermic aspects of pyrolysis, they are aware of these aspects to the extent of knowing precisely when to break open the mound by cues of smell and smoke texture. Opening too soon, before pyrolysis is complete, can coat the branches with earth and introduce too much air into the kiln, suffocating the carbonization in some places and stimulating it excessively in others.

Foley (1986:28) notes that "there does not appear to be any immediately evident explanation why charcoal is popular in one place and virtually unknown elsewhere under apparently similar conditions." Possibly the applied technological knowledge required to repay the effort of forming and tending a kiln is culturally transmitted and simply has not reached places where the ecology and energy needs would make charcoal a good fuel. Also, such knowledge, drawn from experience and apprenticeship, cannot be synthesized intuitively, without experience.

Muindi, a Kikuyu from Central Province, arrived in Eldoret with knowledge of charcoal kiln construction and management that he imparted to Mark, a Luhya from Kakamega, who had not made his own kilns before. Kikuyu kiln making is documented from the 1940s (Elmer 1943), but Kenyatta (1938:73) refers to the varieties of charcoal used in Kikuyu iron smelting without describing how the charcoal itself is made. It's ironic that Kenyatta, initiator of a specifically Kenyan ethnology, and the first president of independent Kenya, should declare that Kikuyu ironwork might seem "primitive in the eye of the machine-man of the Western world" while bypassing charcoal making, which has persisted in practice long after Kikuyu ironwork has become a historical footnote, and which is being disseminated by migrant Kikuyu like Muindi. The machine-man of the Western world still doesn't understand exactly how the Kikuyu charcoal-making process works.

The charcoal kiln is opened by spreading the earth away from the carbonized branches and letting them rest or "season" in place for a time, also decided by experience. Residual pyrolysis might turn into spontaneous combustion if the wood is stored without seasoning. The wood is then broken into pieces that can serve in a stove, and loaded into the common canvas or woven plastic-strip grain bags for storage.

Using charcoal as fuel requires other technologies of design to slowly release and channel the heat energy that is deliberately retained in the charcoal-making process. The interiors of Mark's and Muindi's dwellings are small and well insulated in order to take maximum advantage of charcoal's heating potential. Humans and fires use oxygen and produce combustion products that neither humans nor fire can absorb; hence there is a tradeoff between heating and breathing within these spaces. As with the charcoal-making process itself, a matrix sets the limits of charcoal fire: the size of the space within which the fire burns, the number of people it can comfortably contain, and the times when the burning takes place.

In Eldoret's seasonally cold climate, the charcoal-heated small interior is preferable to the wood-fire-heated exterior because human breathing is not inhibited by the slow radiant charcoal fire and may help to control burning within a small space by consuming some of the available oxygen. Lack of measurements restricts any speculation on the interaction between humans and charcoal fires inside dwellings, but it is apparent that humans have benefitted enough for the specific refinement that charcoal represents to have been developed. This heating system and others are enhanced by the voluntary control of burning provided by the charcoal stove, or *jiko*.

The appropriate technology movement of the 1970s resulted in the dissemination of an improved jiko design that draws air up into the burning charcoal from below through a small door vent that can be regulated (the "Thai pot," Foley, Moss, and Timberlake 1983). This jiko, constructed by trade metalworkers from scrap materials, is available in the Eldoret market, and it is the type Mark employs with full consciousness of its greater efficiency. Also available in the markets, and promoted through the Kenyan school system (Patel and Vashista 1992:97–98), is an hourglass-shaped, welded metal jiko lined with a refractory of clay or cement (the Kenya ceramic jiko, Hankins 1987:44–46); however, it is not as popular because it is heavy, loses its lining too easily, and is expensive. An understanding of energy efficiency has not canceled out cost and portability considerations.

Charcoal is a technology for optimizing a natural resource, but there are natural and social limitations to its usefulness. The wood's potential energy output is limited by the availability of wood and the amount of space in which to enjoy it.

There is a socioeconomic differential in the use of wood as a charcoal source. The large, private stone dwellings, when they are heated at all,

A fundi with jiko

are heated by wood fires, and the cooking is done on paraffin (kerosene), gas, or electric stoves. These dwellings consume more energy than the dwellings of charcoal users, although the same number of individuals may be involved in each case. If calculated on the basis of energy use per person, the total number of BTUs consumed from wood and electricity would greatly exceed the consumption from charcoal. This provides an index of socioeconomic difference: charcoal users consume less energy from that source than wood-electricity users because they cannot afford the equipment to employ those sources. A social division in technology is also a division in capital investment in home utilities. These heating technologies are not comparable in themselves: jiko are not simply a home utility like fireplaces and stoves. Charcoal defines one technological domain that can only be measured against electricity and fuelwood in input/output terms, and even then the measures are misleading because the intervening technologies of shelter, clothing, and furniture modify the human effect of the output. The degree of capitalization of each technology seems to scale them against each other more evenly.

Mark and Muindi are not forced to use charcoal because they cannot use any other sources. They use it because they have always heated themselves and cooked their food this way, and they don't want to squander resources on unnecessary energy they cannot channel. Both men support small families on fixed salaries in shillings. Although both have gardens, the gardens are shared with their employers, who contribute rights over the land, seeds, and implements, but little labor. Charcoal use is another aspect of the voluntary but monetarily exiguous level on which they live. The amount of resources they use, but not the technology they employ to use them, defines socioeconomic class. A British expatriate physician on contract with the Moi University Department of Health Sciences lives by himself in a ten-room house with a full domestic and yard staff, epitomizing the technology/class division.

One technology relates to another on this class basis. It may be that "tradition" decides how the heat need is met, but there are several traditions on different levels, each with its own technology. Charcoal burners and electric stoves both function as working devices, and long treatises could be devoted to how they also function socially to distinguish strata and to integrate these strata (the cook who cooks on an electric stove for an employer may make his or her own meals on charcoal or with paraffin). Charcoal users stand in relation to electricity users as members of groups larger than their technology use alone would describe.

Because it does not just provide heat, one type of technology, charcoal, is associated functionally and in other ways (for instance, culturally) with other types of technology. Its hierarchical relation with electric stoves is only in part a matter of relative energy use, relative dwelling type, and relative income. To speed the igniting of the charcoal pieces, Mark and his wife Grace use a straw fan purchased for that purpose. Also associated with charcoal is a type of cooking vessel that could be used on an electric stove, but is not.

This earthenware pot (*chungu*) has a spherical body and a flared lip with a heavy lid. Its flat foot makes it stable for positioning upon stones over a bed of coals. The food cooked in it is usually a stew of rough root vegetables and maize, placed in the pot with water, covered with the lid, and left overnight on the embers. The diminishing energy of a charcoal fire is of little use for warming enclosed spaces or for active cooking, but it can be accumulated in a design like the chungu.

This passive charcoal technology is replicated in the electric slow cookers available in Eldoret appliance stores. These electric cookers also replicate the difference between charcoal and electricity as heat media, the one retentive and slowly distributive of its resource, the other requiring continual supply into a use with a thick aura. Light-spun aluminum pots of many sizes (*sufurias*) are used over charcoal to boil milk and water and anything that might be cooked in them. These are produced in Kenya, but obviously not on the same basis as the earthenware chungu.

Due to the kind of cooking it provides, charcoal calls for distinct foods. The high-peaked, proximate, and slowly declining output is well suited for the maize, dried beans, and potatoes that are common fare among those who can afford charcoal. Spinach, cabbage, greens called *sukumu wiki*, and a variety of other leaf greens (collectively *mbogu*) are also cooked. "Sukumu wiki" means "get through the week" (and thus fill the belly in the absence of other food) in Swahili. ("Sukumu!" is also what the matatu driver shouts as he tries to pack people into the vehicle; it seems to connote the kind of endurance that both people and plants must have in order to make the trip.) Kenyans identify a number of greens as sukumu wiki, for instance some types of chard or the leaves of the brussels sprout plant, which they eat in preference to the tiny sprouts. Unlike spinach, which it has virtually replaced in Eldoret, sukumu wiki does not crush when transported, and takes much longer to cook, thus lending itself to being left unattended simmering in a chungu over charcoal coals.

Taste varies from one ethnic group to another, and certain vegetables are strongly associated with Kikuyu or Luhya, who consume those (and not others) as much out of group loyalty as convenience. *Irio*, a stew of onions, potatoes, maize, and beans (all of the ingredients historically nonindigenous) is associated with the Kikuyu, although each group has evolved its own version, like the eggplant and tomato ratatouille–imam bayildi stew complex of the Mediterranean. The range of "mzungu" vegetables that Mark raised in the garden for his French employers—broccoli, brussels sprouts, zucchini—also might interest him. Meat and fish and anything else that can be cooked over gas and electricity can be cooked over coals. Cost and availability set the limits more than the nature of the medium or ethnicity.

This passive, home use of charcoal contrasts with an active public use. Roadsides in town are often lined with small jiko on which cobs of maize (and never anything else) are laid to roast. The maize roasters are men and women seeking to enhance income by providing a "fast food" service for passersby, and the low technology of the setup contributes to speed, portability, and cheapness. One ear of corn costs the roaster less than fifty cents (one-half shilling) and can bring three to five shillings. The portability reduces the expense because the brazier can be set up anywhere there are customers. It is often just a pan with charcoal, not even a jiko. The licenses required of hawkers are not usually demanded of maize roasters, although a municipality, or individual police, may decide to "control" them. Sweeps of maize roasters from the center of town at the time of presidential visits have joined other urbanizing forces to nudge the maize roasters and paper sellers up side streets.

The narrow margin of profit can only be meaningful as an expression of rural economy in an urban environment where goods at one price level (raw maize) can be translated into goods suited to a higher price level (roasted, immediately edible maize). Although a colonial law prohibits the growing of maize within city limits (there is a persistent belief that maize plantations promote disease and shelter thieves), maize is in fact grown everywhere in Eldoret—in courtyards, along the road, and in the drainage ditches. There is even a small crop in the drainage channel in front of the police station. A recent Ugandan study (Maxwell and Zziwa 1992) has shown that much of the maize sold by roasters is grown in the cities where it is sold. Only a little charcoal is required to operate a street brazier, which can also be used to cook more elaborate meals.

Most purchasers of roasted maize prefer an evenly exposed ear with few areas of charring. The roaster fans the flame, watches the roasting,

Roasting maize on a grill using a jiko

and turns the ear. A potential customer will inspect an ear, remove a kernel to taste it, and if it is acceptable, pay for it.

Neither Mark nor Muindi roasts corn at home, though they might buy an ear from a roaster when in town. They produce, purchase, and use their charcoal on the urban periphery. Although their technology is the same as that of the roasters, the economy and associations of their activities are different. They might be surprised to hear their home cooking compared with the street work of the roasters.

The charcoal technology does not fit into an evolutionary grade below gas, paraffin, and electricity. Its technology is not any less "advanced"; in fact, some of its refinements may even be more recent than the others. If the other warming and cooking technologies express themselves in watts or cubic centimeters, charcoal has its own quantities and measures that have been studied by those interested in promoting its advantages (Juma 1987). If it does not have the institutes or industries of electricity, it is because it is common and obvious to those who use it. Its function is above all to fulfill a basic need efficiently and without the display and waste in other technologies serving the same purpose. It seems always to have been that way, which makes it seem "traditional" whether it is or not.

When the price of paraffin became unaffordable for a woman who owned a burner, she rapidly switched to charcoal without any feeling of lost status or advantage. It is unlikely that those accustomed to electric stoves and well-provisioned fireplaces could make the same adjustment. Conversely, the tailors who operate on the streets press cloth using irons (*pasi*) warmed by charcoal coals within the iron body; no other type of iron is convenient for their work.

Charcoal is a universal technology for a universal set of needs, but with an eroding resource base. Something like it must have been available for a long time. It seems to have entered the city from the countryside to mark a rural element there, as most African cities retain elements of the rural origins of their migrants. The "white highlands," of which Eldoret is the chief city, have long been one of main draws of migratory labor as people from neighboring farming and pastoral communities come to seek wage employment on the large farms and the factories, formerly owned by white colonialists and now primarily in the hands of

Kenyans (including Asians). These migrants—both Mark and Muindi are examples—have brought with them technologies that suit their livelihood, and while in the same economic situation, they exchange both goods and technologies appropriate to that situation.

Although the use of charcoal remains essentially domestic, commercial uses and a commercial level of production have evolved to meet commercial and growing domestic needs. Charcoal is commonly used in business as a cleaning agent in the making of *mursik*, fermented cow's milk, which is an essential component of the Kalenjin meal. In a production process that extends from the domestic to the commercial, raw milk is placed in hollowed-out gourds, which are then hung for a few days in a warm place, probably in a kitchen or near a jiko. After the mursik is served, the gourd is cleaned out with charcoal, which will absorb any overfermented milk clinging to the inside wall that might sour later batches. The next milk to be placed in the gourd will carry with it the charcoal left there, and thus charcoal has become an essential ingredient in both the flavor and the look of mursik. Those who produce mursik commercially in stainless steel vessels (for instance, in the Mursik Hotel in Eldoret) need to sprinkle some charcoal on the surface to have a recognizable product.

Another product that is dependent on charcoal technology is *nyama choma* ("roast meat"). The freshly butchered cow (*ng'ombe*) or goat (*mbuzi*) meat is roasted in massive hunks over an open charcoal bed, and it is practically the Kenyan national food. A restaurant named The Holiday Inn on Oginga Odinga Street in downtown Eldoret exhibits a folding street sign with a roasted leg on a platter. The retiring American ambassador to Kenya, while being denounced for interfering with Kenyan internal politics, was also praised as a "true Kenyan" because he openly favored nyama choma. Large restaurants in Nairobi have butchery counters where patrons can select their meat cuts and watch as they are roasted to taste over the open pit.

Eldoret has no operation of that magnitude, but in the *jua kali* (artisan) areas are several hole-in-the-wall nyama choma roasteries that consist of nothing more than a charcoal fire and a selection of meat chunks. In each direction outside of town are butcheries with nyama choma places nearby. A party can bring a cow to the butchery, have it slaughtered, feast on its meat, and have the drinks paid for with proceeds from the rest of the cow. The one Asian restaurant in Eldoret, Biharilal, maintains a large basin of cooking oil over a charcoal-fired stone stove in order to deep-fry regular batches of *bhajia* (batter-coated potatoes, onions, and cabbage), their most popular item.

All of these commercial fires have to be maintained throughout the day, which requires a steady supply of charcoal. Even a small nyama choma eatery will use about one-quarter a standard bag of charcoal (about one cubic meter) each day. The total commercial requirement for Eldoret is about five bags a day, the equivalent of a ten-meter-tall blue gum, one meter in base girth, which will yield five to seven bags if it is entirely rendered into charcoal. Not even considering domestic uses, one eight-year growth of tree would have to be felled each day to supply Eldoret's charcoal-using restaurants with cooking fuel.

Most of the large restaurants use paraffin, gas, or electric stoves, but fuels have been increasing in cost despite sporadic government efforts to regulate them. They are not always available, since they are imported and subject to economic manipulations. Long lines of people holding yellow plastic containers to collect their ration of paraffin at local gasoline stations is everyday testimony to the individual problems of imported fuels.

Charcoal seems a comparatively reliable heat source, simply produced within Kenya, but it too has been rising in price as the supply of trees diminishes and the demand increases. Although there is an officially set bag price, charcoal is now sold by the individual one-liter can measure for much more than the official price per bag. (During negotiations for a national raise, the former leader of the Coalition of Trade Unions, J. C. Mugalla, pointed out this discrepancy.)

Charcoal is at a premium, and so are the trees from which it is made, ever more so because there are no systematic programs of tree replacement. On 1 April 1993, the Kenyan Arbor Day, the director of the Kitale Forest Museum complained publicly that plots within grounds designated for preservation were being allocated and the trees cut down for charcoal making. This usurpation of park land is a common ploy of Kenyan "big men," who now have found a quick money-making option in supplying charcoal to urban markets. The politicians and landowners require the services of charcoal makers to exploit their holdings, and thus earth-kiln commercial production comes about. There is also poaching of trees not situated on a plot with the owner clearly in possession.

Downtown Eldoret has few stands of trees, mostly ornamentals, and few eligible for charcoal. Various construction operations have been preceded by the felling and kiln-burning of the trees. Charcoal making is ceasing to be a casual act because property rights are exercised over the trees and charcoal making is now associated with further commercialization of the land from which the trees must be removed. Because a house is being built on their kiln plot, and there are few trees to fell, Mark and Muindi await another chance to use their skills. For now, they can no longer make charcoal but must buy it from suppliers. The economics of charcoal captures those with the technological skill in a narrow functional zone and creates a complex that will lead to the termination of earth-kiln charcoal making—the end of a technology for lack of materials and circumstance. This is best seen in one case typical of Eldoret.

The land near the Eldoret Club is being cleared rapidly for building the large stone houses favored by the Asian population and resident white foreigners from Europe and America. An empty lot opposite the only large wooden house in Eldoret (the "Morgan house," built by an early tour operator during the 1940s) was owned by a pair of Asian brothers, who had already sold an adjoining plot on which an Asian family had built an enclosed compound. They now wanted to improve this waste lot to take advantage of the paved road spur of the service lines already extended. They planned to build a stone house, which would rent for a good price due to proximity to the club and the State Lodge.

The lot was lined on one side by a row of decaying cypresses, the legacy of the owners of the Morgan house, and it contained several tall blue gums, two avocado trees, and a number of grapefruit and orange trees that yielded large quantities of extremely sour fruit, as well as a large amount of herbaceous and woody brush. The residents of the recently built compound constantly complained to the owners that the growth in the compound might harbor thieves, giving them an additional inducement to clear the lot.

The landowners hired three young Kikuyu men with experience in the array of tasks required, and it was agreed that the men would do the work and live in one side of a divided brick storage building in exchange for the right to make charcoal from the wood obtained. Additional work on the house to be erected, for instance the preliminary brick making, was to be compensated separately.

After they cut down all the grasses and shrubbery with pangas, the men started with the bordering cypresses, some of which tilted over the only road to the Eldoret Club, threatening both traffic and telephone lines. They had to prevent the trees from falling into the road when cut, so they set up bracing lines, fastening one end of a thick rope high on the trunk of the tree to be felled and the other end to a sturdy upright tree in the center of the lot. They then cut a notch in the trunk on the side of the proposed fall, and when the tough cypress fibers were just strong enough to balance the trunk on the stump, they pushed it over toward the side of the cut. The men hired a worker with a gas-powered chain saw to do the initial cutting, and they also used the chain saw to cut the trees into one-and-one-half–meter sections. The cypresses were felled in a row parallel to the road, with only a few left standing to serve as props. The men trimmed off the branches using pangas. After they had finished five cypresses, and while the chain saw was still available, they attacked the large blue gums scattered in the lot, and then the orange and grapefruit trees. The women who forage for firewood were kept away by the continual presence of the men in their on-site quarters.

The next step in the process was to separate the wood logs from the branches. The cypress logs were stripped of their bark, split into quarters, and stacked in crisscross layers behind the brick house, reserved as fence posts to encircle the lot (where they once had been trees). The cypress bark, branches, and the other trees were all destined to become charcoal.

Over a period of weeks, the wood was piled into kilns, covered with earth, and burned. The kiln design called for an orderly stacking, larger branches toward the bottom, and the whole covered with dried grass and earth, forming man-sized mounds. Smoke filled the area where there had been growth. After they opened the spent kilns, the men added any unpyrolized wood to the next set of kilns, and in this way all of the wood and brush was heaped and converted, bagged and carried off.

After the heavy work of clearing was done, one of the men found employment as a gardener nearby, and another left to work on other projects. The remaining worker, Mwangi, lived in the brick hut, kept the lot clear of new growth, and organized kilns around the stumps of the trees. Since he had access to a regular water supply through a tap in the garden, he was able to keep himself and serve as host to others, providing them with accommodations and an opportunity to cook and do laundry. He was able to construct a modest household on the strength largely of his charcoal production and thus integrate himself into the local economy of workers.

As the supply of wood for charcoal production petered out, he began digging postholes and setting the fence posts for the multistranded barbed wire fence that was to encircle the property. When the owners of the lot delayed construction of the stone house, Mwangi found a job digging postholes on the periphery of EATEC property fronting the main highway. His payment for this work was the same as for his clearing labor, the right to make and sell charcoal from wood collected off the wattle plantation that the fence surrounded. Mwangi used his bicycle to carry the long, horizontal sacks of charcoal to the market in town.

This was the last work-for-charcoal-rights arrangement Mwangi was able to make without losing the situation he had created for himself on the now cleared and fenced house lot. Charcoal making had moved out of the town precincts, and if he wanted to continue, he too would have to move farther out of town. These areas, chiefly settled by Kalenjin people, were also the scene of tribal clashes in which Kalenjin youth attacked Kikuyu settlers and burned their houses. Charcoal making was associated with the Kikuyu, and only an organized corporate entity like EATEC, with its own uniformed, multitribal police force, could practice commercial charcoal making or allow charcoal to be made on its land.

Mwangi turned back to his home base. The owners had decided to raise vegetables on the lot, and they reengaged Mwangi to work the land where his kilns had been, under the supervision of a Kikuyu lady who specialized in high-yield urban farming. Any trees grown there would be ornamental and not for charcoal. Without the material of their application, the charcoal-making skills are nothing but history.

5. The Land

Technology seems a male province in Eldoret, and women and children only its passive beneficiaries or victims. If the focus were to shift only a few kilometers in any direction, along Uganda Road toward Webuye, along Kisumu Road or across the plateau into Iten, the relationship between women and technology would be far more visible. The work of these areas is agriculture, and women have been the primary agriculturalists—"have been" because the introduction of agricultural technology predominantly operated by men is having increasing influence upon the apportionment and working of land. With tractors (bought, serviced, and frequently seen in the city itself) and the amazingly large combines (which also challenge the width of the main road in the city), more land can be farmed in the countryside. The capital, force, or guile required to build up anything more than a smallholding sectioned out at independence have mainly been employed by males. Extensive planted areas owned by absentee capitalists are spread along the peripheries of Eldoret.

The land in Uasin Gishu District has long been contested. Its pleasant upland climate, good soils, and equatorial sunlight appealed to colonists with ambitions only large holdings could satisfy. It is the only area of Kenya, and one of few in East Africa, suited to large-scale cultivation of maize, millet, and wheat (Odingo 1971). Labor rather than machinery cleared the land, planted the seeds, and harvested the crops—African labor supervised by Europeans.

Since the area was underpopulated for the purposes of the colonists, they imported labor from the Rift Valley, where people had been expropriated by large-scale agricultural enterprises (Carey-Jones 1972).

During the early years of the century, newspaper advertisements promising fertile land drew South Africans to Uasin Gishu, who subsequently found themselves shunted over to the less fertile plots by the British colonists. Kamba, Kikuyu, and other Kenyan peoples began a migration into the highlands that continues to this day, and movement into urban areas forms the other important migratory pattern within Kenya. Thus, Eldoret, the largest city in the highlands, has been doubly endowed. Adding to the complexity of the mixture are families of Turkana and Samburu pastoralists forced by drought in the far north of the country to make the trek south into the farming region.

The question of who lived on the land prior to the advent of the Europeans is subject to debate among Kenyans. One group with a strong claim came to be called Kalenjin, which means "I can tell you, because you understand my language," a commonly used expression. The Kalenjin are a set of groups (tribes or clans) speaking related and mutually intelligible languages (Sutton 1976) who inhabited the highlands but had long been subject to incursions by Maa-speaking peoples pressing down the Rift Valley. During the 1940s, Kalenjin leaders came to appreciate that they needed to form a collective front if they were to play a role in the national life of an independent Kenya and hold their own against the more numerous Kikuyu, Luhya, and Luo.

When with independence in 1963, the Kenyatta government awarded title to lands to Kikuyu and others who had migrated into the highlands, the Kalenjin felt they had been denied land that had been theirs before colonization, although the Kikuyu also considered themselves the dispossessed prior possessors. The Europeans and Asians simply migrated to other parts of Africa, causing a slight dip in the Eldoret population despite the continued influx of Kenyans (Mbwagwa 1980:35).

The efforts to remove "outsiders" from the land continue, and the advent of a "Kalenjin" government under Kenyatta's successor, President Daniel arap Moi (a Tugen, one of the smaller Kalenjin groups in the Rift Valley), has facilitated this, but certainly not with the wholehearted concurrence of all Kalenjin. Tribal clashes in the areas around Eldoret are attempts by some Kalenjin to facilitate this removal, and by others to resist it and avenge themselves. However, Kalenjin control of the land has continued to increase because larger sections of land have come under the control of individual Kalenjin, who in turn seek to obtain yet larger holdings by encouraging the clashes and arming the young "warriors" who burn the houses and shoot the occupants.

Whatever its ideological complexion, the struggle for control of the land is between smallholders and the capitalists who seek to continue what the Europeans began: production of massive cash-crop yields that can be sold abroad for better prices than at home. Tribal differences are at base economic, and economic differences tend to become tribal.

The peoples in the highlands have long jostled each other for land and raided each other for cattle as part of complex strategies for such purposes as managing population growth and using disputed resources. Where groups identified as Kalenjin opposed non-Kalenjin, they have been able to secure government help in carrying out their depredations.

The foreign-managed colonial government was not consistent in its pacification policies, often favoring one group to "police" others who had to be rendered harmless as opponents of European policy and gains. For example, a Kalenjin sub-group, the Nandi, were ferocious adversaries of the British, but after their defeat at arms, they were equally ferocious recruits to British forces (Matson 1972).

In Bungoma, northwest of Eldoret, were battles between the Kalenjin Sabaot and the Bukusu and Maragoli (two subgroups of the Luhya who, like the Kalenjin, also are a collection of numerous smaller groupings). The Sabaot actually are an Ugandan group who have asserted rights to Kenyan land from which they claim to have been dispossessed when Kenya and Uganda formed the British Protectorate of East Africa. Their grievances are one international issue manipulated by Kenyan and Ugandan politicians with their own land interests. Like the Maasai in the south, the Sabaot have been used to drive Luhya and Kikuyu settlers off land the Sabaot claim was their own.

During the height of the clashes of early 1992, it became difficult for farmers from the Kitale or Kakamega areas to move their produce into the Eldoret market. There was an informal ban on non-Kalenjin-operated matatus crossing from the Luhya zone, and it was necessary to change matatus once or twice before arriving at the market in the ethnically correct manner. This raised transport costs above the profit margin for some farmers. As part of the tactics of economic warfare, "bands of Kalenjin youth" (as the *Nation* described them) stopped matatus on the main roads from non-Kalenjin areas into the city, stoned those without the requisite personnel, and even roughed up non-Kalenjin passengers.

There was no violence within the city, even though a letter was circulated threatening Kikuyu and Luhya shopkeepers with reprisals if they did not leave before a stated date. Those who were threatened made an appeal to the district officer. The day of the deadline, most of the shops were closed, but no mobs of warriors appeared to carry out the threats.

However, similar letters were circulated in Nairobi and Kisumu to Kikuyu and, on a later date, to Kalenjin shopkeepers, and there were serious riots. The Asians, who own most of the shops (and employ both parties), were neither threatened nor attacked, though it is true that for the most part they have avoided having anything to do with agriculture except as investors, plantation managers (Kumar 1987), and technicians.

The clashes are the most dramatic outward manifestation of land conflict, but they are accompanied by, and may facilitate, Kikuyu selling land to Kalenjin in areas of Kalenjin predominance, and Kalenjin selling land to Kikuyu and Luhya in areas of Kikuyu and Luhya predominance. These land sales apparently are leading to greater ethnic consolidation and the threat of what in Kenya has been called "majimboism," a doctrine of separate land-based polities for separate ethnic groups (from *majimbo*, the plural of *jimbo* [nation]). It cannot be too strongly emphasized that neither the Kalenjin nor the Kikuyu form a unified, coherent group with a recognized common purpose, despite announcements that parties or individuals may make to justify their own actions.

The technology of warfare, and of reaping the fruits of warfare, appears to belong to males with tribal identities. One consequence of the redistribution of land has been a decrease in women's productivity, which typically has been centered in the household. Even the common occupation of a market woman is an extension of that. Families tend to invest education funds in male children, and the urban, salaried employment that is only available with education most often goes to men (of the right ethnic background). Women have picked up subordinate and secretarial positions in the cities, but not to the extent of the high demand for office workers occasioned by, for instance, an oil industry (as in Nigeria or Iraq). Also hampering female enterprise is the widespread belief that any woman who enters the city other than as the wife of a man who goes there seeking employment is bound to become a prostitute. It is as difficult for a woman to leave her home area as it is to establish herself in the city.

Stichter and Parpart (1987) point out, however, that attitudes might change if women's presence in the city serves capitalist enterprise, as in the Zambian copperbelt cities, or if women succeed in becoming capitalists themselves, as is increasingly true of Eldoret. "Prostitution" in Nairobi and other Kenyan cities was a way for women, sometimes refugee women, to earn a living by providing a range of domestic services, including but not confined to sexual services (White 1990). In the wake of the tribal clashes, women who fled to Langas established a brothel with the significant name, "The Hungry African." However, this is by no means the only or the most typical example of women's enterprise in Eldoret, where women work as tailors, hairdressers, produce vendors, secretaries, attorneys, and doctors.

Nevertheless, women's production continues to be defined by access to land, providing for children, and maintaining a household. Loss of land limits that production because it replaces the familial base of production with a corporate base, and replaces production mainly for subsistence with production for profit. Production then becomes linked with reproduction of a labor force (Meillassoux 1981).

This transformation of women's work from household-based to for-profit labor in the urban economy has gone largely unreported in Kenya, where women have been, and largely remain, people without history. A recent edited volume of themes in Kenyan history (Ochieng' 1990) contains twenty chapters on such subjects as transport, health, and cooperatives, but not a single chapter on women. But merely including women in recognized categories, or creating a new category for them, will not redress this exclusion. Warren and Bourque point out in their general review of research on women, technology, and development ideologies that "adding gender as a category of analysis to current social science involves more than just recovering women's experience. Rather, gender differences call for the explanation of male/female inequalities, much as the study of cultural constructions of racial differences calls for the explanation of racial inequalities" (1989:389).

Women have not opposed the introduction of technology when it has enhanced the existing agricultural production and the capacity of people to live directly from the land, which also affirms the territorial security of the family. In fact, they have been an important medium for the introduction into rural areas of certain technologies such as water storage and grain dehulling through local women's groups and agricultural extension services. It is a matter of encouraging open-mindedness and providing training and equipment that will give women access to technology (Ventura-Dias in Ahmed 1985:210).

The ethnic economics of land use has not favored women whatever their ethnic loyalties. It therefore has not favored children either. The men control the land and receive the tractors as well as the associated training (Morley and Lovell 1986:55). A glance over Eldoret and its surroundings shows this is so. However, what may be apparent in the aggregate can look very different for the individual. Broad phrases like "the expropriation of women as a result of male access to technology" have to be qualified. The areas under the curve may exhibit probabilities quite unlike the trend of the whole, and show the variety of components in the general trend.

Emily is a young woman of the Bukusu, one of the largest subgroups of the Luhya whose area of concentration is about Webuye, a town dominated by a papermaking concern. Webuye is about thirty kilometers from Eldoret on the road leading north to Turkana. Emily's family owns land near Lugulu, a small market town, or rather a market that is a de facto town because that is where people bring their products to make contact with the main road's traffic.

Emily is married to Seringo, and together they have four children, three boys and a girl. Seringo has worked with a number of medical missions and in the process has obtained various health care certificates that qualify him to open a clinic if he could afford the four to five thousand Kenyan shilling start-up costs (equal to sixty to seventy dollars in U.S.

currency). For now, he and Emily work their eight-acre parcel of land with help from relatives, whom they help in turn. They cultivate maize, beans, and pineapples, and tend the banana and papaya trees. It is all manual labor on the sloping fields overlooking a beautiful perspective of the valley before Mount Elgon. Two oxen shared with Seringo's brother made some of the work easier until one of the oxen died while plowing. This setback forced the family to abandon plans to set the lower field in maize and reduced an income that, due to the previous year's extended dry season, was already perilously low.

Emily and Seringo consider a cash income necessary because the three boys attend an excellent private school. In addition to fees for tuition, books, and uniforms, the school requires all students to live in the school dormitories at additional expense, no matter how close their families are. Students also must provide their own bedding.

Like other women in the area, Emily had been able to earn needed cash by taking some of the more easily transported fruit and vegetables to market in Lugulu, Webuye, or Eldoret. However, as with Seringo's clinic, a sizeable fee for a space prevented her from establishing herself in the larger municipal markets where there is a constant flow of customers. Even if she had the money, Emily might find herself excluded because the Eldoret municipal council favors sellers from farming cooperatives over individuals. Emily therefore joined other women of similar status alongside the road, selling small quantities of produce. She was able to pick up sufficient cash for school fees, but never enough to finance a more profitable enterprise.

Emily found a salaried position in Eldoret as a maid, or "house girl," working for an elderly professor at the university. Her monthly wage was six hundred shillings, later raised to nine hundred. This freed her of the uncertainties of casual selling, but it required that she live in Eldoret and travel home only at her employer's pleasure. Since she was the only domestic in a large house, her numerous duties kept her very busy, in addition to which she had to maintain her own separate establishment in a semidetached unit, including paying for the paraffin for her stove and, of course, for her own food, although her employer did occasionally give her some meat. Thus Emily was working apart from the family she was working to support, and contributing to the creation of a domestic space elsewhere in order to transfer the difference in money back home.

Apart from her employer's grudging sufferance, Emily was dependent upon the matatu industry for transport back to her home. The prices of matatus fluctuate with demand and fuel cost, and holidays are the most costly time to move people and goods. There was always a liability in having a job where she did. When her employer's demands became excessive and she wanted to quit, she considered selling in the markets again, but it was always the margin of income she had achieved that reconciled her with her position. Only the loss of her steady salary would reduce her willingness to remain at her job, and her family's support for her commuting.

The failure of the agrarian base to support even those with enough land is a major cause of women leaving agrarian household production and seeking other revenues in the city. Kakamega, an area noted for the small amount of acreage available per person (Hoorweg and Niemeijer 1992), now receives more in remittances from men and women working away than it does from its own agriculture. Emily's labor transfer is part of a pattern that may be directly related to the formation of large holdings and the mechanization of agriculture in the greater Eldoret area. As the large holdings with the capital for tools of mass production become more efficient and acquire more land, the land itself is less able to support its dependents.

Families like Emily's exist in a paradoxical space, still farming the land but unable to maintain the economic stability that farming requires. Those who aspire to escape from this cycle believe it will be mainly through giving the next generation an education, a service the state no longer provides. The rising cost of schooling makes it impossible for Emily's family to make this investment. If the family does not have enough cash income, the first to sacrifice an education will be her precocious daughter Irene, followed by her twin boys, leaving the eldest boy to finish schooling, though perhaps not all of secondary school before he too must seek employment, on the land or in the city.

Women are not so much forced off the land in this type of case as they are required to support the agrarian life of their families by selling domestic labor for cash. This only becomes possible with an efficient road and transport system. The city that serves as a market and storage place for rural commodities also facilitates a market in services, which allows, or obliges, women to assume a role in the urban economy while eliminating what social latitude they may possess as wives and mothers in the household. Emily is in the ambiguous position of being able to win an income by translating her domestic skills, practiced before in the complex social and emotional milieu of the family, into domestic service outside.

Diana is slightly older than Emily, one of twenty-four children from a polygynous household near Timboroa, off the main road leading from Eldoret to Nakuru. Her family are of the Elgeyo, a very small Kalenjin group. She was sent to attend a private school near Nairobi and eventually obtained a degree in elementary education as well as special training in the Montessori method. While working in Nairobi as a teacher, she met Andrew, a Dutch Kenyan citizen employed by one of the development authorities. They were married, and when Andrew, who had obtained a graduate degree and was teaching at the University of Nairobi, was offered a position at the newly formed national university about thirty kilometers outside Eldoret, they eagerly moved back to the area where many of Diana's relatives were living.

One brother had built a gas station, the only one on the main road for some distance. Another had become a permanent secretary in a government department and owned a large house in Eldoret. When a large parcel of land near Cheptiret (fourteen kilometers outside Eldoret) became available through bank foreclosure, Diana and Andrew were able to purchase it. Owning land and establishing a shamba completed Diana's move back to her homeland.

Since her three children reached young adulthood not long after the purchase of the shamba, Diana considered herself free to dedicate herself to farming. She had been intensely involved in women's organizations in the Eldoret area, and especially in trying to educate women in government-sponsored agricultural improvements. That involvement arose out of a combination of regional-tribal-family loyalty and KANU (Kenya All National Union) party politics. (Until 1992, KANU was the sole party.)

While Diana started a dairy herd and planted some of the acreage in maize for silage, Andrew continued his university career and supported Diana in her enterprises. He maintained that it is typical for women to begin businesses once their child-rearing years are over.

The couple kept a small house in Eldoret while building a more permanent residence close to the town and constructing another stone house at the shamba. An entire family was in constant residence at the shamba to contribute labor and guard the herd. Diana sold milk to the dairy cooperative, leaving numbered five-liter cans at the roadside to be picked up each morning. With her profits, she purchased a lorry and leased it for long-distance haulage as well as using it to transport her own products. She found that if she could deliver milk directly to some bulk users in town, she could get a significantly higher price per liter than that offered by the dairy cooperative. The profits obtainable with independent delivery encouraged her to expand her cows' milk yield, which she did by managing feed and silage cycles and monitoring the health of her herd. The increased daily yield was enough to make it decisively profitable to use the truck for deliveries.

The work on the shamba had by this time exceeded the available manpower from the resident family, relatives, and hired labor. A tractor increased the acreage that could be plowed and the efficiency of hauling supplies. Diana also obtained a share in a small combine purchased by several other shambas in the area. This machine, which often malfunctioned and required parts not easily obtained or improvised, marked the limit of technological saturation on this shamba.

Diana represents a set of relations between a woman and technology quite different from Emily's. The input/output structure of relations becomes clearer by enumerating the quantities involved: how much Emily or Diana earns and to what degree their earnings actually are enhanced by their particular access to technology. This account merely outlines the ways in which technology has affected their lives and does not characterize either as an indicative sample.

Change in technology has brought Emily and Diana into a relationship with the land that reflects the social changes taking place in the Eldoret area. Both women were raised to fulfill the productive roles expected of women in rural society, and whatever these roles may have been in their respective settings, their transformation is most clearly charted through contact with technology. Emily has been drawn off the land and into the city by her ability to market her domestic skills, which transport enables her to transfer. Diana, on the other hand, has returned to the land as an agricultural entrepreneur, marketing produce for cash and supporting the families of the women who work for her.

Both Emily and Diana define the manner of the loss of smallholdings and the roles women performed upon them. Where those roles are still performed, they are in the context of larger-scale operations managed by men, who also operate the lorries, tractors, and combines. Diana may manage her shamba and the men who run the machines for her, but she in turn is beholden to male bankers and politicians to sustain the development of her land. An oil pipeline from Nakuru to a newly constructed depot outside Eldoret passed near Diana's property to the profit of her neighbors. If Diana's situation represents the transformation of a woman's domestic role into one of enterprise, then her neighbors' sale of land for the pipeline is a projection of the men's domestic role into commerce.

The pre- and post-colonial roles of men and women in production seem to replicate themselves in every successive economic state. The land and its workings are less under the direct productive control of women as more mechanized technology is required for those workings. A woman who obtains more than a subsistence parcel must immediately depend upon men to work it, finance it, and market the gains; a woman who has less than a subsistence parcel must engage her labor in a male-managed urbanizing economy.

In Kenya, as in the West, people tend to devalue urban life while upholding rural life as a moral and social standard for the entire society, but urban life does offer some rewards. In the countryside, people are subject to familial and communal control within a system of local chiefs inherited from the colonial period (a system the colonists invented, though they claimed only to be formalizing an existing institution). For younger people and women, the city may be a morass of depravity, but it is also a chance to achieve freedom from rural controls.

African cities are often cited as exceptions to a theory developed by

European and American sociologists that the city would prove to be a place where the organic solidarity of rural life would be lost in the mechanical solidarity of the workplace and anomic loss of identity (for example, Abu-Lughod 1961 on Cairo; Mayer and Mayer 1961 on East London, South Africa; and Dutto 1975 on Nyeri, Kenya). This view has recently been attacked in light of more recent developments in these very cities, which show the consolidating effects of urban ideological movements such as Islamic fundamentalism and anti-apartheid.

The tendency to migrate into the city as families and form ethnic communities there, combined with the retention of rural links through remittances and frequent visits back home, has turned many African cities into concentrated extensions of rural life rather than distinctive centers of their own. What differentiates the African city from its own hinterland is the presence of styles of expression from abroad, which are attractive because they are imported and can hold their own against the rural onslaught.

Ownership of land outside the city therefore becomes an ideal integration of urban life, with its cultural and economic links, and rural life, which remains a moral and political base. Although the image of the urban official who goes off to his shamba on weekends may be an oversimplification, it is a fair model for describing the preferred balance of life. This dual role for men might also explain why a decreasing number of women occupy land and control the technology of enhanced production.

According to Maria Ventura-Dias, a sociologist of rural life, "women prevail in areas where no new technology has been introduced, and they are the first to be displaced from tasks that can be commercialized and/or mechanized" (in Ahmed 1985:159). The life balanced between country and city is male; the life in country or city is female. The outcome is impoverishment of women.

Although the argument of Esther Boserup (1970) that rural women lose out when men gain access to technology has become classic, it has spurred amazingly little research. In Eldoret itself, the large number of male artisans of rural background demonstrates how unequal access to training and capital is at the heart of what is described as "urbanization." The differences between men and women in access to technology, and all that it means, are stronger than ethnic differences, and may in fact be replacing them. The supposition that urbanization eliminates differences by forcing diverse groups into contact with each other is questionable both ethnically and in terms of gender in Eldoret.

As she looked out over the vast fields of wheat owned by the Kalenjin MP Nicholas Biwott on the outskirts of Eldoret, at a time when the wheat should be drying and hardening for harvest, Emily, a Bukusu, said with a world of significance, "It is raining on Biwott's wheat." The wealthy, male ethnic opponent could still suffer with his foreign crop the setbacks a rural woman like Emily faces in her own work.

Anne, a Kikuyu woman who has a small shamba near the Huruma estate on the outskirts of Eldoret, keeps a table at the Eldoret municipal market. She sells produce from not only her own garden but also the wholesale lots, from which produce is brought by matatu. Her table is among other women in what has come to be recognized as the Kikuyu section of the market.

When a group of Kalenjin attacked and burned her relatives' shamba in the Burnt Forest section, her relatives fled to her and remained until the fires died down. When they returned, they found the farmstead occupied. Kalenjin were pasturing cattle on their farmland. They went back to stay with Anne until they could move to Central Province.

Anne says the time is coming when all the Kikuyu will have to move from Eldoret and the vicinity back to their own region. They already have been driven from the town of Kapsabet, high in the hills across the Rift Valley from Iten, and now it is almost impossible to buy fresh fruits and vegetable there. Like other market women of Kikuyu, Luhya, and Kalenjin origins, Anne is not teaching her children the "home language." Instead, she concentrates on training them in Swahili and plans to introduce them to English. That way her children can play with the children of women of other groups in the market because they will all have a common language. Perhaps a common language will make it more difficult for them to fight with each other in the future. For now, however, she thinks of leaving Eldoret.

Grace, on the other hand, has no reason to leave. She owns and operates the Nu-Wave Hair Salon in the Eldo Center, a shopping plaza near the post office. Besides the conventional cutting and plaiting for women and haircuts for men, she offers aromatherapy and massage treatments that appeal to her mixed clientele of Europeans, Asians, and Africans. She has also added a typing service and fashion consultation to her business. With two sons in college in America, she needs to earn as much as she can.

Grace's business, overseas experience, and marriage to an Asian engineer seem to reduce her Kikuyu identification. She has invested in a complete refitting of her shop and does not think of leaving. Together with some Kikuyu women advocates (lawyers) and a woman physician who have opened a practice in a new building downtown, Grace has a profession entirely in and of the city. These women, with their husbands, own houses and small pieces of land in a residential district on the outskirts of the city, but they have no time to garden. Instead, they leave the groundskeeping to gardeners, while an askari looks after the premises. The land has released them.

6. Inertial Balance

Many of the men who travel into Eldoret ride bicycles. Unlike the expensively clad recreational cyclists who fly along American and European highways, the Kenyan cyclists wear the usual everyday garb and ride to work or transport goods on heavy imported cycles without gear shifts. The bikes often have to be walked uphill, and they do not move very quickly downhill. In this they resemble the bikes used by the majority of urban workers in the world, in India and China, and in fact those countries supply most of the bicycles used, since Kenya does not have a bicycle industry. (However, Kenyans are so adept at maintaining and adapting existing bicycle frames that the country does not have an industry only in the sense that bicycles are not produced for mass export.)

The mechanism is the same, but the riding of cycles is a technique that makes the technology special. Most clearly, it is a technique more of balance than of motion, but it is balance in motion under the force of inertia. This balance value is most visible in the loading of the bicycles; or rather, the loading of the bicycles most clearly evinces the importance of balance. This is another case in which a mechanism known to the observer is so fundamentally contradicted in an observation that the particular use of the mechanism observed can seem quaint or charming.

In my native technosphere, bicycles are recreational vehicles, and I experience their balance as a delight of independent forward motion that has never gained a competitive edge. If a bicycle is loaded, it is with camping gear, and in a manner carefully designed to serve the same motion I expect of an unburdened bicycle. Eldoret bicycles are loaded and ridden according to a different sense.

Man balancing cases of soda bottles on a bicycle

The bulk of the load placed on the rear rack of the bicycle seems to be unlimited. Large sacks stuffed with cloth, charcoal, or leaves (commonly sikumu wiki); wooden planks that may or may not be canted at an angle; automobile batteries and pieces of furniture (full beds, chairs, tables)— all are fastened in place and carried by cyclists to their destination. The development of the load seems primarily horizontal. The vertical stacking of cookware and boxes up to several times the height of the cyclist, visible in India, Thailand, and China, is not a common sight.

It would be rash, however, to form a cross-cultural generalization about the kinds of balance on this evidence. The Eldoret cyclists do favor lateral dispersion about a central pivot in motion, whereas the Asians favor aggregation at the pivot, but all will carry whatever they need to carry by the available means. There is no opportunity to make a comparison within Eldoret because the Asians here do not themselves transport goods by bicycle, although a few favor the imported stylish, athletic ten-speed mode.

In addition to goods, cyclists carry people, at times on the same bicycle. The passenger, a man or a woman, sits upon the rear and clearly partakes of a balance sense similar to that of the loaded cycle's operation. Women sit sidesaddle, and men usually legs astride. It is a camaraderie of shared balance and a coordinated competition between balancing cyclists who rely on each other's skill to avoid accidents.

The society of balance is maintained apart from the mechanism itself. In an act of balance that could be seen as a metaphor of social order, I have seen an entire family disposed along the frame of a bicycle: father on the seat, child on his lap, mother on the rear rack holding an infant.

Cyclists carry their loads along the paved road, where they are relegated to the sides on unaccommodating shoulders or none at all, where they have to avoid vehicular traffic. They also travel along the many footpaths, either riding or walking. To maintain upright balance with the loads they carry, the cyclists must keep up a certain speed and possess the ability to hold the bicycle stable when they cannot go fast enough. They must know exactly the point at which they should quit riding and take to walking. A capsized loaded cycle or a castoff load can cost a great deal of time and revenue if the goods are damaged. An accident with a passenger would have much more serious consequences.

Masinde raises chickens on his plot outside Eldoret, and once a week he cycles the ten kilometers to the Eldoret market, where he delivers five to ten pullets to a selling agent. This supplements his income as a casual laborer. He looks forward to the time when he can afford a space of his own in the market.

Masinde used to carry the chickens, immobilized with tied legs, by stacking them on the rear rack of his bicycle and binding them there carefully with cord. This did not always work so well because the chickens could not be bound tightly enough to keep them in place, nor loosely enough to keep them from suffocating. Masinde therefore invested in a circular cage that he could mount on the rear rack with the chickens inside. Their legs were tied, but they moved around the cage with changes in incline and light as chickens do, and Masinde found himself needing to compensate from side to side a great deal as he rode. This problem was intensified by the strong side winds that swept across his course and threatened to carry him into traffic or into the drainage channels by the roadside.

Masinde recognized that by moving faster, he could overcome most of this distortion of his travel, but the increased speed required more careful maneuvering, not always easy with his bicycle's battered front wheel. He also found that he had to violate the order of the cyclists by the roadside. There were not many on the main road, but as he neared town, their numbers grew. As they streamed alongside him, Masinde often found himself unable to go slowly enough to satisfy an order set by the bicyclists carrying larger, bulkier loads. If he wanted to pass, he had to move out almost into traffic because the loads on the other cycles were often very wide.

The other cyclists would make what allowances they could for him to pass, either moving as close as they could to the edge of the road or even parting to create a corridor for him to move through. Only under very crowded conditions, when other cyclists with light loads were competing for the same movement, did he find himself obliged to yield and slow down or race to keep ahead of the fastest. His only near-accidents involved motor vehicles, not cyclists.

Those with heavy and bulky loads find that they need to keep up an average speed in the line of cycling traffic or pass into the faster zone that Masinde and other light loads occupy. The slow speed is usually enough to maintain balance without forcing anyone to become destabilized or ride at a pace that machine or muscles cannot sustain. The sense of balance in the cycling line is vested in the motion of most loads that can be mounted. This inertial balance is a complex adaptation to the bulk and density of the typical load, the nature of the instrument (human and mechanical), road life, and transport economics. It is both a cognitive and social adaptation and it is not limited to bicycles and their riders.

Kenyans have the mechanical ingenuity to devise a more efficient technological solution to the transport problem by introducing gear shifts or loading platforms as has been done elsewhere. However, the technology and the balance comport with other factors in the adaptation, and for one to change, the others would have to change, or be changed. The inertial balance that is the chief cognitive feature of the cycling line is a prerequisite for maintaining a uniform speed and distance between cyclists.

Male children do not cycle in Kenya until they are large enough to operate the standard-sized cycles without faltering. For most Kenyan children, there are no infant cycles or training wheels. Such devices are used mainly by European and Asian children, who rarely venture onto the open roads. Kenyan children begin riding when they have a reason to, and when they are prepared. A boy whose legs barely reach the pedals can occasionally be seen standing as he pedals along an open paved road, but no doubt the bicycle has been borrowed for the occasion with considerable warnings.

A new bicycle costs from 3,000 to 5,000 Kenyan shillings (equal to about fifty to seventy dollars in the United States), and the price is always rising because bicycles are imported. Such a purchase represents an outlay of two to three months' earnings, so only a well-paid worker will buy a new bicycle, and only if the purchase will repay itself. Used, very used, cycles are commonest, and knowledge of cycle repair comes with learning to ride.

Bicycle repair shops, which may be no more than collections of parts and tools, are common features of shop rows and roadsides, and most cyclists carry materials that can be adapted to common cycle repairs. Kenyan languages each have bicycle part terminology, which can be quite figurative, but English and Swahili technical terms are also freely used.

A man entering upon a set of adult economic relations has to begin cycling regularly. However, the system of balance among the cyclists is simply a socially advanced form of a balance sense that children already possess. Men come to cycling with the cognitive skills already developed, needing only the financing and the particular occasion for that type of transport.

The technologies of this precocious inertial balance are visible everywhere, but nowhere more clearly than in the training of women. It is an article of gender identity that women be able to carry loads upon their heads. Men can do this, too, and are occasionally seen doing so, but the laboring profession of male headload carriers, a major proletariat in South India, is absent from Kenya. When men must carry heavy weights, they suspend the load upon the back with both arms at shoulder level.

Women carry on their heads everything that men carry on bicycles (even furniture), but they leave commercial transport to the men and generally carry only for themselves and family members. This division coincides with a larger, legalized exclusion of female labor from the value sphere. The male employment of technology (bicycles, carts, trucks)

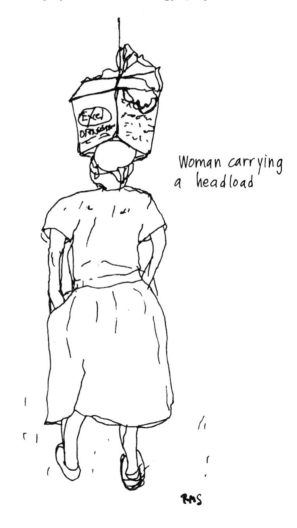

Woman carrying a headload

sanctions the value of their work, while the absence of technology from the women's head-carrying, and its personal or familial basis, seems to mark its lack of concrete value, its role as identity rather than as work.

Women learn this carrying procedure as men learn to ride bicycles, as an implementation of an existing balance, only they begin using it at a far younger age. Both the act of carrying and its accompaniments (what is carried, as well as the purpose and manner of carrying) are associated with feminine character.

Young girls begin carrying small loads on their heads soon after they begin walking. Coached by older women in how to raise and support a load, how to steady it with the hand but not to rely on the hand to hold it there, girls quickly become adept and eager for ever larger and heavier loads. A girl might at first rest a pot on a firm woven grass ring (*mviringo*) atop her head, but older girls and adult women scorn this aid unless the load is so unevenly distributed that it will not stay.

With birth spacing as it is, by the time a girl is ready to carry objects on her head, she can also carry an infant sibling in a cloth slung over her back or across her front, another aspect of her identity as a woman that she will bear her entire life. These components of what a woman carries are balanced around forward motion since they are to be carried from one place to another and not merely supported. That forward motion in complex balance becomes a feminine quality: the right arm bent at the elbow and extended at a slight angle to the body, the head erect whether bearing a load or not, the pace measured and straight ahead. Feminine grace is described in these terms, and women's dance is a variation upon this state of balance. When a man wishes to imitate a woman, he knows exactly how to convey the desired impression through this variation of the common balance.

Men's early expression of balance includes toy technology, like the wheeled toys described earlier, as well as rudimentary weapons and tools that men are expected to use as adults.

Kenyan children are able to walk very early in part because their parents allow them to participate soon after birth in acts of balance. A child is carried on a woman's back, suspended in a broad kerchief, which is fastened by tying together the ends in front. The child rides here while the woman works in the fields or carries a heavy headload along the road, and mother and child are so mutually integrated into this act of balance that sometimes the child only becomes apparent up close, or because the woman must make an unusual movement.

Thus, infants soon learn the manner of balance and have experienced motion over the terrain by the time they are able to stand. The pattern begun in childhood then serves to organize more specialized acts of balance in gender and occupational differentiation. As further development of erect posture and walking refines the balance that precedes their achievement, independent movement becomes socially codified in gender and work.

Walking is the most basic use of inertial balance. In walking, the potential of the individual body is given social form subject to further variation. The quality of walking as technology is visible wherever people walk in masses, but it is especially noticeable in the adaptations of those who must move but cannot walk in the established patterns.

In any concentrated population of walkers as in Eldoret town, there are some people whose disabilities make it difficult for them to match pace and gait with the others. These disabilities may have resulted from nutritional deprivation or infantile poliomyelitis infections that occurred before widespread vaccination. Even today, polio or rickets can severely damage the legs of those too poor or too remote from medical facilities to receive proper care.

The success of some of those afflicted in achieving participation in the walking is remarkable. With legs bent sideways at the knee, or twisted thigh sockets, they maintain the same speed and rhythm as the other walkers, and support comparable loads. The fundamental balance that they share with their compatriots does the work of unavailable prosthetics, crutches, braces, or wheelchairs. It appears that the common balance makes it possible not to define these people as community liabilities requiring special treatment. The walking mass moves forward with them.

Yet more remarkable are the severely disabled people whose withered, twisted legs leave them unable to stand, no less walk. Although a few have handpedalled or wheel-maneuvered wheelchairs, others must move unaided, which means crawling. They use their arms as legs might be used, protecting the hands, elbows, and knees with cushions. They also are accepted into and move with the stream on the same basis as all others. The inertial balance is not solely an attribute of erect posture, but its origins in being carried as infants allow it to apply as a social form to people of all physical attitudes who must take part in the common movement in ways that look unusual only to an outsider judging on a purely mechanical basis.

The Swahili words for cripple (*kiweka*) and blind person (*kipofu*) place these and other disabled people in a noun class reserved for objects (*kitu*, "thing"). While a language's grammar is an uncertain key to the thoughts and sentiments of its speakers, there may be something to Louis Leakey's observation of a related language, Kikuyu, that these nominally rejected beings nonetheless "DO possess a human spirit" (1959:2) in the view of the speakers. Their position in that noun class, like their position in the crowd, shows them to be things that are human.

Msemba is a shoemaker, *fundi wa viatu,* who unlike most of the shoemakers on the streets of Eldoret has a tiny shop of his own. Located on a raised walkway between a bookstore and hardware store, the store would be easy to pass by were it not for the wheelchair always parked outside when the shop door is open. Msemba has withered legs, the result of a childhood infection that was not treated in time, and his profession of shoemaker would seem to be an ironic choice since he is supplying items he himself never could use. This does not matter to Msemba or to his customers.

To be a good shoemaker, you must have strong arms and fingers, and these Msemba has from propelling himself manually all his life. He is able to translate the sensations of walking with his hands into the making of his shoes, and to give these shoes a feel for the balance which those who need shoes require. He can cut the leather patterns and use a heavy needle to pierce the sheets with that balance in his very fingers (although this may be overintellectualizing his ability to handle the tough materials of shoemaking with more adroitness and concentration than others).

His wheelchair is driven by a bicycle pedal gear mounted in the center of the seat. As he rotates the pedals with his hands, Msemba moves a chain that engages a gear in the axle below and causes the front wheels to move. The ratio of the upper to the lower gear is great so that with just his arms, he can power himself up the steep hills of the downtown and control his descents. The tall rear wheels permit him to hand-drive the wheelchair where required.

Msemba needs the skills of both walking and cycling to move about the downtown, which is not at all handicapped-accessible. The pavement, where it exists, rises in small, steep steps and falls in precipitate grades, and often it is broken or interrupted by obstacles that narrow the passage, so Msemba travels on the roadway, which can be in the same condition. Besides his own strength and skill, he relies on the cars, trucks, and cycles on the road to be in the same system of balance. In its location and size, Msemba's shop is a demonstration of his ability to negotiate this world successfully.

The walking spaces of downtown Eldoret are more difficult for able-bodied foreigners to negotiate than for crippled natives, primarily because foreigners do not at first share the balance. And they may never share it if they continue to demand an environment that provides familiar cues, when the cues reside in the people. Neither the language nor the food conveys the sense of difference more fully than the walking environment, which is *not* made to travel through on foot but rather is a goal of travel (and the creation of a variety of forces to be discussed later).

Walking, though it is the chief means of locomotion, is only minimally supported by the city's structure, which comes as a surprise to anyone familiar with the esplanades and boulevards of other cities where walking is invested with enjoyments (and threats to those enjoyments).[1] Eldoret was constructed for other reasons. The inertial balance system permits necessary passages that otherwise might be hazardous. Even where there is no even surface or invitation to walk, large numbers of people can pass uniformly, continuously, and without incident.

A capacity for smooth crowding is a corollary of balance that adds to the evenness of urban rhythm. For instance, on a narrow rocky defile between a drainage ditch and the roadway, lines of people readily establish themselves moving in both directions. When people stand and speak with each other in the middle of the most heavily traveled walkways, the passing crowd will bunch itself to get past. Matatus and minibuses discharge and take up their passengers in the midst of well-traveled routes.

The outdoor produce, goods, and clothing markets at the heart of the city sustain continual walking movement without inviting or facilitating it, particularly because the movement is uniformly presupposed to be based upon a common balance not forced by planning or architecture. The mass of people is greater than the village or household groupings, but it keeps its movement and ignores obstacles on the same basis as smaller groupings. Crowding is not alien to experience, and every individual is already fixed in a social system that urban crowding simply promotes. The only difference is that in an urban crowd, an individual may find himself next to someone of a decisively different cultural background. Then it will depend upon the constitution of the crowd whether symbols or balance will prevail. In daily passages it is mostly balance. Anyone who is different from the main can refer to balance to keep a common interest, just as he can speak Swahili and share the experience as a Kenyan. If he is challenged to speak Kikuyu or Kalenjin, then the crowd experience has excluded the common identity to emphasize another kind of solidarity.

The urban crowd in Eldoret is not the sinister organism that it has been in European experience, from the French Revolution to the mass social movements of the twentieth century. That is, it has not been a threat to public order and individual safety because it is primarily a transport device and a continuing expression of smaller-scale associations based upon a common *kind* of identity. The person next to me may be of a different background, but he has the same kind of background I do.

There have been incidents of "mob justice" in Kenya lately when crowds that formed in response to an alarm have caught thieves in the act, or suspected thieves, and have stoned, beaten to death, or necklaced them (the term for having a petrol-doused tire set ablaze around the neck), and then burned the bodies. The ultimate reasons for the increase of this activity may be frustration with economic inequalities (which a thief is trying to cancel out the easy way) or the failings of a corrupt criminal justice system (bribeable police who never bring a thief to justice).

In Eldoret, a young man who tried to rob a kiosk with his friends was caught and killed by the mob. He was a Kikuyu, and so were those who killed him. His sister expressed no criticism of the mob's action: she regretted his death but felt he had brought it upon himself. Whatever the ultimate reason for an attack, the victim of a mob has done something to separate himself invidiously from the mass to which he belongs. Their immediate violent act rights the imbalance. Kin and friends of the victim recognize the principle.

Usually an aggregating crowd is forming out of curiosity to watch the aftermath of an accident or an appearance by a public official. It is not difficult to attract a crowd, but because of its moving nature, it is difficult to sustain people's attention. Street musicians and ranting public preachers only gather a few casual onlookers, never an audience. Public demonstrations that address the existing political system rapidly attract the forces of order, which seem to be political agents of balance.

A group of women, mothers of political prisoners, attempted a public demonstration in Nairobi, and both they and those they attracted were attacked by the police. The women defended themselves by removing their clothes, a not unfamiliar tactic, as scholarly articles in the newspapers pointed out later. (A male officer would not dare approach or even look at a naked woman in public for fear of reprisals from her kinsmen.) The group of mothers then retreated into the Anglican cathedral, where they were again attacked by the police, after which they began a fast. The attention their publicly expressed sentiments was drawing, and not the sentiments themselves, seemed to be the reason for the roughness. Crowds mean interest, and dissipating a crowd dissolves the interest, or such seems to be the logic of the forces of this order.

Balance in motion and the tightness of crowds shape the forms and uses of technology to serve the group in its whole. People move in balanced crowds, and so the technology of movement reflects that. The bicycle is the single vehicle of balance within the milieu, and its riders move in crowds on bicycles rather than as cyclists in crowds. The mass transit vehicles—buses, trucks, and matatus—permit the mass to move together in a state of balance they do not need to achieve through their own mechanism. The social effects of balance and crowding govern the transport of

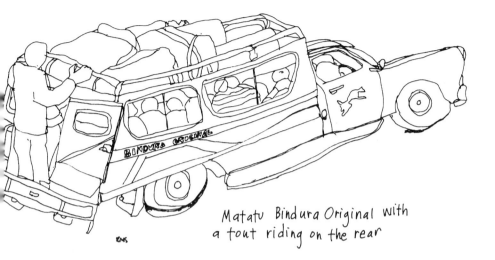

Matatu Bindura Original with
a tout riding on the rear

these vehicles. (The engineering and repair of the motors is an entirely different matter.)

Transport as a crowd is the primary mode. It would be foolish to assume that this is a cultural form in its own right, and that people prefer to travel as crowds because it maintains inertial balance. Inertial balance and normative crowding propose a style of travel suited to the economics of transport. Ever more people are fit into small vehicles when they can tolerate dense packing arrangements and have the freedom to innovate in their attachment to the vehicle.

The name *"matatu"* is Swahili or Kikuyu for a "set of three (ten-cent coins)," and it supposedly is derived from the thirty-cent fare charged when the transport was initiated in competition with the more expensive buses (or from a remark Jomo Kenyatta made that the fares were all "just thirty cents"). A matatu is generally an enclosed cabin mounted on the rear chassis of a Peugeot 405 pickup truck, though other vehicles are used. Against the side walls of the cabin are two facing benches where the passengers sit.

The statutory limit on matatu passengers is seven, but a matatu would not move with so few. The *manamba*, or tout who serves as matatu conductor, supervises the loading of the cabin until the sustainable limit has been reached. He obliges those sitting to make room, and detects any space that might be used to site another person. He orders large people to adjust themselves to make room for smaller ones, and when the seating space around the perimeter is fully occupied, he introduces men and women who will bend or crouch in the center of the cabin. After that arrangement is complete, those who will hang off the back, including the tout himself, hold on, walking along behind the vehicle until it picks up speed and they can jump on, clinging with their hands while resting their feet on the bumper. The maximum I have counted in this arrangement is twenty-one adults. Only men cling to the back (I have seen ten), which encourages a public show that women, tolerant of any state of interior crowding, tend to reject.

On the roof of the matatu are stacked goods in transit, the property of the passengers, and commercial carriage. Matatus carry bicycles, furniture, large quantities of produce (even the cabin might be filled with potatoes or sacks of maize), and chickens laid upon the roof like lumber. Many of the passengers are transporting rural products to the regional market in Eldoret. Since most of the sellers in the market are women, and women customarily do not ride bicycles except as passengers[2] (and generally live so far away that bicycles would not benefit them anyway), the matatu owners can demand a significant share of a woman's market revenues to provide transport. With matatu transport, as with bicycle transport, there is a complex profit-and-loss minimax strategy, which is tempting to characterize as an economic extension of balance.

The matatus are owned by enterprises or individual entrepreneurs who provide the vehicle and (perhaps) its upkeep. The other main operators of the matatu mode are the driver and the tout, who receive a share of the take for each trip. Both are legendary figures in contemporary Kenya. Many drivers pride themselves on the speed with which they can carry along these loads of passengers and goods, challenging other drivers along the road, yet able to detect and stop for a passenger waiting by the roadside. The drivers need to know how to maintain a matatu to prevent breakdowns and how to rapidly repair a vehicle should a breakdown occur. Any disability is loss of trade and a serious detriment to the owner and to the tout. The pressure of mechanism is on the driver, and in speed is balance.

The owner provides the financing and sets the rates, the driver the direction, and the tout the style and packing skill. The tout dresses with flare, speaks a smart urban melange of Swahili and other Kenyan languages called *Sheng*,[3] and has perfected the manner of walking behind the matatu. As it starts up, the tout, with one hand on a side rail, matches his pace to the increasing speed of the vehicle until at the last moment he rises onto the rear bumper of the matatu, joining the others clinging there. The act is a lyric in the language of balance.

The Sheng word for the tout is *batteri*: he powers the enterprise like one of those colorful pieces of paper or genuine batteries that boys place in their wheeled toys. When urging passengers to squeeze in closer, an Eldoret tout will say something like, "Sukuma, sukuma, kita mtu akae square, ndio hao coopaa, wee nama pale bendoa mandiaba, unakaa ndee unafikiri kati ni ya bwanako, kaa square kama farasi." ("Squeeze, squeeze, sit straight, there are cops around, you lady over there, do you think this is your husband's? Sit straight like a horse.") One time a man approached the rear of a matatu, looked in, then turned away, saying, "Too crowded." The tout called to him, "Nafikiri ni yai tu?" ("You think you're an egg or something?")

In part because of the large number of people traveling in a single vehicle—matatu, bus, minivan, or private car—Kenya has a high annual rate of motor-vehicle deaths: more than five per one thousand vehicles, compared to one per two thousand for the United States and Japan. An accident that might leave the solitary driver injured can kill one of eight people in a packed car. The larger number of passengers per vehicle is a difference in the economics of vehicular transport, but also one of technology.

Whereas municipal governments in the United States have been hesitant to penalize drivers of empty cars even during peak hours, the Kenyan system operates to minimize this abuse—but creates the opposite. People depend upon the availability of that one more space inside an already full vehicle to obtain transport. Taxis and transport with assigned seats are rare. The Peugeot to Nairobi leaves when it is full and takes three and a half hours to reach a destination five to six hours away by private car.

The automobile engine and drivetrain have created a great opportunity for Kenyans to turn their sociability into a technology that maximizes transport spaces. As long as that maximum sustains itself inside a moving vehicle in balance with the inertia of motion, all arrive safely. But the exception, the accident or the odd breakdown, is damaging in the same way that any failure in a presumed and fundamental order is comprehensively destructive. Balance is life in motion, and its failure is death on a scale that only the magnified energies of technology can cause.

7. Electricity

The line voltage supplied to Eldoret is a fluctuant 220 volts at 12 amps. It is derived from the Kenyan national supply net originating in hydroelectric power plants on the Tana River (some 400 kilometers away), on the Turkwel River, and in Uganda. As of 1979 (Fadel 1979:15), there was a 132-kilovolt line running from Kindaruma on the Tana River to Nairobi, and thence to Mombasa on the coast and west to Eldoret and Uganda. When production drops from the Tana plants, which can lose voltage during the dry season, the Kenyan net is designed to facilitate purchase of electricity from Uganda, which generates more power than it needs from the falls at the origins of the Nile.

Generating facilities were increased for the Tana and Turkwel Rivers, but both power augmentation projects have been attended by considerable controversy. The Turkwel project, completed by a French concern under contract with the Kenyan government, has been associated with high-level corruption and is said to be structurally unsound as well as unable to generate the anticipated output. The plans and construction record of the project fill an entire section of the Kerio Valley Development Authority library in the KVDA building in Eldoret. As the new facilities came on line in the 1980s, the national net was upgraded to make Kenya less dependent upon expensive imported oil, at least for power generation, and upon, at that time, politically unstable Uganda. (In fact, the pylon train from the Turkwel was designed to intersect with the national net at Lessos, about thirty-five kilometers to the south of Eldoret, avoiding proximity to the Uganda border.)

Eldoret is a supply center on a mixed basis, which means that the national transmission line enters a substation here for local distribution, and oil-fired steam generating facilities are also in use (Ojany and Ogendo 1973:180), though they now function only in emergencies. The main substation, set by the highway in an open field, is a set of deck transformers within a chain-link enclosure (which has no "High Voltage" signs). The transformers receive the supply cable and originate lines in a radial transmission system down several roads and to the textile mills along the main road. There are step-down transformers periodically along the line, which yield branch lines and a collection of separately fused streetlights.

The residential, commercial, and industrial supply is very reliable, with fewer outages and interruptions of service than is usual in most American or European power-delivery settings with more secure distribution networks. That regularity seems almost completely imperturbable. An attempt to "ration" power during a low water-supply period during the early months of 1992 was never really enacted as widely as announced. This was in part because the supply system in many places lacked the instrumentation to cut power for the specific periods of time demanded, and because so many exceptions were given. If power had to be supplied to a hospital or to an official residence, then it had to be supplied to a large portion of the surrounding town as well. However, Kenya Power and Lighting periodically announces in newspapers the shutoff of power on stated dates and during stated hours in named places about Kenya.

Electricity in Eldoret has primarily been used by the affluent because of the capitalization required. Electricity is to a fair extent an ethnically defined realm because the main purveyors of electronic equipment, and its main consumers, are members of the large and complex Indian (Asian) community, with consumer participation by Euro-American expatriates. Once more, level and type of technology are governed by level of income. As evident in the previous discussion of the use of charcoal, technology type seems to represent the major socioeconomic and ethnic divisions in the community. The use of electric appliances provides further evidence of these divisions.

Cassette players certainly are the most visible and audible appliances. A large variety is on sale, ranging from modest one-tape portable decks to effulgently silvered two-tape systems with multiple speakers and graphic equalizers. In early 1992, the prices ranged from about 1,000 to more than 8,000 shillings (equal to about $15 to $120 in the United States).

Since all of these devices are imported, their prices rise as the shilling loses value (from twenty-eight to the dollar, to forty-five, and then to seventy-five during 1993). This means that even the simplest system is beyond the reach of the average Kenyan wage-earner (about 1,200 shillings a month), even on the lease-purchase terms offered by several stores. The larger systems are clearly for household use only and not for hand-carrying as in the portable music culture of American cities. The ostentation that makes them a valued accessory also relegates them to the family circle in Eldoret.

The simpler cassette players do appear in public but not in the possession of individuals. They are used to play tapes at the numerous stands and street vending locations in the downtown areas. The stands are wooden enclosures that blast music into the air near the central market, from the depths of the movie theater building, and through the jua kali area near the bus station. The street vendors lay their cassettes in neat tiled arrangements under overhangs on the streets (always the same places). Ubiquitous tape boys sell them directly from boxes, with their own version of Sheng patter.

Prerecorded cassette tapes, along with wristwatches, wallets, and socks, are the major ware of hawkers, but they are kept separate from other products. The tapes are purchased in lots by Asian merchants, who then give them to hawkers to sell on commission. The hawkers, who seldom own their own stock, are mobile and thus able to elude police, who demand that they show licenses or pay bribes. The greatest danger any hawker, stationary or mobile, faces is confiscation of his wares.

Since the most mobile sellers lack the facilities to play the tapes that they thrust at anyone who has paused long enough (sitting in a matatu, waiting on a street corner), they attempt to circulate near a cassette player broadcasting music from one of the shops or street displays. However,

Hawker with
cassettes

the hawkers represent competition that the settled sellers do not like, and sometimes they have to take advantage of their mobility.

The mobile hawkers rely upon the familiarity of the music they are selling, either of the names (Kanda Bongo Man, Dolly Parton) or the type of music (cha-cha, *tsaba-tsaba, bololo*). The buyer will presumably recognize the common types, and after that, all the hawker needs to do is get the money. Merely a glance at the title of a cassette will bring a persistent and insistent address. Hawkers course down the streets flashing the tapes at anyone they encounter, attuned to the turning aside that might mean a sale if they follow it up quickly enough. In a sense, they are using caloric energy where they cannot appropriate electrical energy to push their wares.

The more sedentary street sellers have cassette players but no access to line voltage, so they rely on batteries. However, batteries to power even a small player are an expense not clearly justified by the business drawn, so some of the street sellers use auto batteries. They keep their players operating by attaching clips and a cable to the electrodes and feeding it into the battery springs of the player, evidently at the correct polarities. Others change the scale of the technology and have available a Walkman with earphones to audition tapes for customers (*customa* in Swahili).

It seems an aspect of the energy economy that the tapes are all sealed and all pirated. They are produced at facilities, accurately described as factories, in Taiwan, China, and other areas of East and Southeast Asia. The technology to produce multiple copies of a single tape and package it in sufficient quantities and at sufficient speed to be profitable simply does not exist in Kenya. Even Kenyan recording artists see their music available on the street in pirated versions before the studio versions have been distributed.

Showing the same aptitude they did in copying Western consumer goods (from American Wheaties to the Australian condiment Take-A-Break), the recording pirates concentrate on the packaging. The recording itself, numerous generations away from any studio master and beyond any considerations of high fidelity or stereo, is more recognizable from its packaging than from its sound, which will be (or should be) heard through equipment of comparable low fidelity. Because of the production requirements of those faraway duplicating units, songs are often cut off halfway through, making a mockery of the also-pirated paper insert with its list of hits. This much, however, is by no means peculiar to Eldoret or Kenya, but is a sign of the market dependence of Kenyan consumers upon other, more developed economies for goods they do not produce to the extent their own markets demand.

From mode of manufacture to method of advertising and sale, cassettes are predicated upon a technology that cannot make use of line voltage and is battery or human-powered, all the while manifestly depending upon the availability of line voltage in some form. That the public exhibition of cassettes is dependent almost entirely upon failing, costly, and weak sources of energy (compared with line voltage) does not in itself account for the absence of soundscapes common in North American, South American, European, and Asian cities. Kenyan radio stations broadcast voice or music all day long, but not at high relative volume. Because the broadcast signals are so weak, there are no waves that battery power can raise to high levels of audible sound, thus the noisy atmosphere that even an inexpensive radio can create is unknown. Automobile radios are available, though not generally to the degree of elaboration or wattage known elsewhere. Their ownership is uncommon enough, yet prestigious enough, that it is unwise to let it be known that one has been installed in the car.

An exception to this generally subdued sound quality is the flashy colorful urban matatu or minivan (*manyanga*), becoming commoner in Eldoret, with a speaker system that can play cassettes at greater volume. The manyanga itself is a complex technocultural image that evokes style and flash just as *mitumba,* second-hand clothes, evoke dullness and routine—hence the Sheng expression, "Hii dem alikuwa manyanga lakini sasa ni mitumba tu" ("This woman was with it but now she's just old clothes"). With the speaker system, emphasis is on raw volume, not acoustic power. There appears to be no concern with reproducing the rich bass tonalities edited into most popular music cassettes (if they are even available on these pirated versions of the cassettes).

Since the speakers are inside the cabin of the matatu, the volume heard on the street is incidental. A recent campaign in which the Nairobi police began apprehending and fining drivers of matatus sporting loud systems revealed that the lyrics of the songs were more offensive to the authorities, and perhaps to the passengers, than the volume of play. The songs, and the touts and drivers who select them, sometimes criticize the ruling KANU party or praise the opposition parties. Songs also may be "obscene" by Kenyan public standards, which under a constitution that makes possession of "pornography" a punishable offense are strict standards indeed.

Letters to the newspapers during the height of this campaign expressed a range of sentiments from weariness with the blare of the speakers in crowded matatus to defiance against the authorities for their attempted suppression of dissent. Matatu touts rioted against police trying to enforce the ban. Since the matatu is also a social technology, a compromise was reached, and the matatus still belt out their songs in Nairobi. It may be that the flowering of the minivans, with their loud color combinations and often gruesome names (Cannibal Love, Scorpion Love), is visual expression where the auditory has been suppressed.

The political nature of matatu volume marks it as unique amid the relative silence. Breaking that silence has to have a special meaning. Eldoret, as the main city of the president's home region, is still guardedly silent on that score.

The matatu noise is accomplished by cassettes at one end of a lively industry of political and social comment limited by the unavailability of means. The battery-powered cassettes played in the street or amplified out of a matatu are as much as any opponent to the regime can afford or expect to have financed by like-minded people. The production of films is limited to the careful and well subsidized and is done primarily by overseas interests appropriating Kenyan locales (*Out of Africa* or *The Air Up There*). A festival of Kenyan films shown in Nairobi concentrated on clinical advice documentaries made for a national media outreach program, whose green and red mobile cinema trucks are still visible about the city and whose films may occasionally be seen in the countryside, shown under generator power. (This does not mean that Kenya lacks skilled filmmakers, men and women, but merely that they find it difficult to get backing for their work.)

Video technology has begun to enter the city in a manner similar to cassettes, though exhibition of videos can never be liberated from line voltage. There are two video shops, one a stall beside the KANU office and the other a full-scale video rental center in a shopping plaza. Other stores rent or sell a few videos. Their main fare is pirated American and Indian movies, and their main customers are those (mostly Asians and Europeans) affluent enough to own both a TV receiver and a video-cassette player. Since the equipment and the voltage are not affordable to the popular audience that videos have in other settings, there is no street sale of video cassettes. However, there are video exhibition parlors.

Sosiani Videoscope is a room near the central market where two or three videos are shown daily, beginning around three in the afternoon.

The films are the same ones available in the video shops and shown at the movie theater (when it operates)—violent American action epics and Indian romantic adventures. The video parlors, and the one restaurant that also has a video exhibition schedule, bring the equipment to a general public that has no other access to video. Though the nature of the medium determines the conditions of exhibition (indoor and confined), there is also something of the privileged quality of line voltage in its exclusiveness as opposed to the more or less democratic power of the cassettes. Video production has also become available on similar terms. An entrepreneur who manages to secure a video camera and a playback deck can earn a living taping weddings and other celebrations, but such men advertise their services, not their exact whereabouts, because cameras are a livelihood in themselves and can be stolen.

Line voltage in Eldoret is a privileged energy source. Those who lack access to it benefit from electricity only in the form of streetlights and the outdoor playing of cassette tapes or indoor video showings. This sharpens the distinction already apparent in the comparison of the electric stove to the charcoal burner, which shows the social division between those who use electricity and those who depend on other means.

The contrast between use of electric stoves and charcoal burners is near the extreme of the division, as is video technology, which is used by very few and viewed by only a few more. Cassette players come at a breaking point, powered by line voltage or battery in a variety of arrangements, but still a stationary technology because of the investment it represents. Line voltage is an interior and private (or commercial) energy technology in Eldoret. This status means that there are few alternatives, and that the sense of emergency when line voltage fails is confined to the downtown and the residences in the immediate vicinity.

The protocols of line voltage do not structure the ecology of energy use and transmission in Eldoret as they do in large cities and in other countries. Electricity helps to maintain an interior space and machinery for industrial labor, sales, and a type of domestic life. The places it creates are under the control of those who have financed their creation, which usually means official or business figures. These places are accessible to those who themselves cannot capitalize the installation, supply, and use of electricity. The distribution of electricity at social nodes rather than evenly along the lines is evident from the construction of the transmission lines themselves, with step-down transformers and off-lines at irregular intervals. These nodes are centers where people who do not have line voltage in their own dwellings can make use of it, while aware that it is extended to them through the group or institution that serves as a patron.

Consider the large dwelling of an officer of one of the banks in downtown Eldoret. The man is the sole formal inhabitant of a two-story, eight-room structure. He spends his days at his office downtown and most of his evenings at the Eldoret Club, where he eats dinner and plays cards with other local businessmen. He visits his wife and children in Nakuru every weekend. However, his dwelling is never unoccupied. There is a live-in maid with her own detached dwelling, a gardener who works in the yard during the daytime, and an askari, or guard, who patrols the perimeter at night. They all make use of the house's supply of electricity while at their tasks, yet none have line voltage in their dwellings.

The technology may be democratic in its potential, but the actual distribution is to the regular inhabitant of the house, who has control over switching and use. As with food, the others get the leavings of the produced commodity but do not consider it essential to their well-being. A bank officer or any other official would not accept living in a house without electricity; he must be in a *position* to use it, and to be a source for other people's use, which he at least nominally controls.

Those who are located to consume line voltage are also situated to own the appliances associated with it, and they might consume lavishly and very conspicuously, with color televisions, food processors, and rice cookers, except that social systems limit this capacity and occasion other systems to modify it further. Anyone situated to draw a heavy and continual flow of current must also be prepared to pay the escalating price of higher levels of use. The schedule of charges employed by the Kenyan Power and Lighting Company (a government-managed corporation) rises geometrically with growing use. So while a person must be advantaged to have control of the apparatus to receive line voltage in the first place, he must be at a yet higher level to make the demands expected of a patron upon whom family members and other clients depend for this and other bounty. Because KPLC is a public entity operated through a ministry, a user's official status can modify the actual charges.

Another control upon the overutilization of electricity by those positioned to do so is theft of the apparatus. The more portable appliances can easily vanish from inside a dwelling, as can the fixtures. The very size of a dwelling is an indication of the presence of these items. It is easy to judge what conveniences the owner's prestige would require that he possess. That is why security gates and askaris protect the perimeters of these dwellings, and also why thefts still take place. The askaris, who are drawn from among those without line voltage or appliances, might submit to be bound for a share of the proceeds. The stolen objects are sold to others in large houses with outlets, and so the cycle goes.

Actually, an interesting moral axiom—that consumers must pay in proportion to their rate of consumption—operates in limiting the consumption of line voltage. The operation and ambiguity of this axiom is suggested by the workings of the KPLC. Its charges and billing procedures enforce the rapidly increasing expense of greater use. The bills are issued from a central location in Nairobi and show the likeness of Reddy Kilowatt declaring, "I worked all these hours for you . . . for only this much pay." A failure to pay the full sum of the charges will bring a disconnect notice on the next bill. Further failure to pay will bring to the door of the dwelling (unless you are of high enough status) a man on a motorbike who will claim he needs to read the electric meter. Since meters are read at mid-month, but this man arrives at the end of the month with a tool protruding from his pocket, his declared intention is hard to accept. If given access, he will remove the main fuse after having shut off power at the main circuit breaker, and the current will remain disconnected until the bill and a sizeable fee are paid.

If the disconnector fails to gain admittance, he or his successor will threaten to cut the wires at the supply line. Since all supply lines in Eldoret run from the main line in a radial series, the cutting of the line that runs into the offender's unit means turning off the supply to an entire group of dwellings. The single dwelling is not the unit of supply or of disconnection, and any disconnection must be of concern to the others on the line. The group is inconvenienced for the failings of the one. The moral axiom is made linear. Scoffing at the power company brings retribution, but since those who are responsible for paying the bills are themselves a privileged elite, the retribution is deferred and softened. Its agents have to ask permission to perform the disconnection, resort to trickery to gain their end, and make unrealistic threats if unsuccessful. The moral principle remains a principle.

The power company's road crews also function morally to limit power consumption while maintaining the supply to the privileged. Though their composition is defined in terms of competence in maintaining the transmission lines, their membership is mostly restricted to Kalenjin, the dominant ethnic group in the Eldoret area. Since the Kalenjin are themselves a composite of several groups with closely related languages, the crews favor those Kalenjin (Elgeyo and Tugen, the "president's group,") most heavily concentrated in the Eldoret area. A man who had served as an assistant to the engineers of a telecommunications company, and who had gained much practical knowledge of electricity in the process, was told that he did not stand a chance of getting a job on a road crew because he was a Luhya from Kakamega and not Kalenjin.

This restriction, easily labeled "tribalism," is also a moral function of the technology of power provision. Someone who is not Kalenjin will not understand the language normally spoken by the crew members, while even the most electrically naive Kalenjin will be supported and trained by the rest of the crew. In their hands, sustaining power is not just a technical commonplace but an act of supplying "their" land with the motive force of development. It is employment denied on the basis of ethnic affiliation, but it is denied to outsiders by way of affirming a hard-fought control that is both concretely economic and mystically ethnic.

The KPLC line crews require strong solidarity to function as required, cooperating to restore power during the night rains or holding the rope attached to a fellow crew member atop a ladder to keep him clear of the wires if he falls. What members of the excluded groups may view as tribalism and corruption is seen by those who get the jobs as part of the moral whole that includes supplying and controlling the supply of electricity as a cultural group.

If the Kalenjin have acceded to this control over the moral supply of line voltage in accordance with a larger cultural politics, the Asians have achieved another kind of control over the fittings of electrical supply and the appliances. Because they are the shopkeepers and wholesale merchants of Kenya and Eldoret, they provide the technical services and the equipment for the commercial and domestic enjoyment of line voltage.

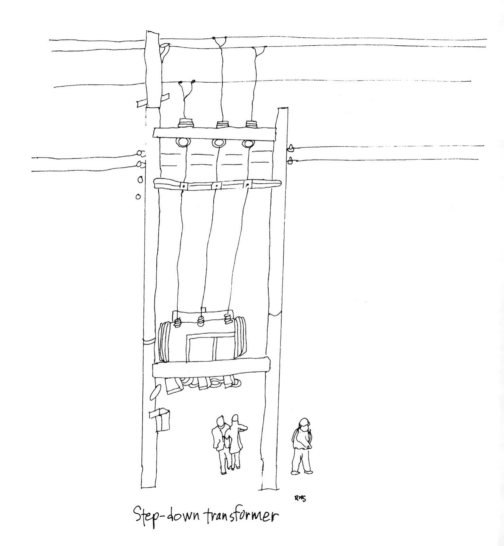

Step-down transformer

Where the Kalenjin leave off, the Asians begin. Their stores even supply the cassette players that break away from the economic internals of line voltage by running on batteries.

One Asian-run electrical shop in downtown Eldoret is GEPS, Limited (General Electrical Products Supply). Stores in Eldoret are still stocked according to the bazaar principle and tend to specialize only in "hard" or "soft" goods. The supermarkets that are a recent development in the city's merchandizing may carry both hardware and cloth items as well as groceries. The bookstores, which really specialize in selling school books and supplies, generally do not carry electrical fixtures, but the clothing stores might carry cords and outlets.

GEPS is an electrical and gas goods store, part of an Asian-owned chain that has stores in major cities throughout Kenya and does not sell anything but appliances and electrical goods, and it carries electrical items that no other store is likely to stock. It is, for instance, the sole source of 220- to 110-volt step-down transformers that will operate high-wattage equipment. While most appliances imported into Kenya (from Europe, India, and East Asia) are designed to run on 220-volt line voltage, occasionally an American import requires a transformer. American expatriates, mostly well-provisioned missionaries for various denominations, bring their own computers, printers, and other devices unavailable in Kenya, and they need to ensure a current supply at the appropriate voltage. Transformers may malfunction due to improper matching with appliances or electromagnetic induction during violent thunderstorms. Surge suppressors and voltage regulators may be required. AC to DC transformers may need to be replaced.

The Sikh proprietor of GEPS is, as the Kenyan law provides, the master of a shop that employs a number of Kenyans in clerical and technical roles. The Kenyan employees operate the test equipment—bridges to determine the viability of transformers and appliances—and select parts for customers, but the proprietor is the arbiter of complex devices and large purchases. He may serve as electrical consultant or subcontractor on building projects. His expertise lies in knowing how to bring together a variety of devices from suppliers outside the country to function under the supply and regulation that prevail in Eldoret. To maintain this position, he must be able to match fixtures with devices both mechanically and electrically. The numerous kinds of plugs and power requirements make it necessary for him to have a comprehensive knowledge of currently available fittings over a wide range. Like an auto parts dealer, he must be able to improvise a safe substitute for a use that has no standard part. He works close to the abstract nature of the medium in having to satisfy an unpredictable demand for specific instances.

In a residence where the rooms were not all provided with electrical outlets but only with lamp fixtures, it was impossible to place three-prong outlets into the fixtures because these were no longer manufactured. Mr. Singh knew that attempting to operate high-wattage grounded equipment through lighting fixtures was likely to cause a fire. In an office where several low-wattage transformers had burned out attached to imported equipment, Mr. Singh discovered that high-wattage equipment was being operated on the same supply line, causing a surge through the system that the low-wattage transformers could not sustain. The solution was to give high-wattage devices their own lines. These are the kinds of problems Mr. Singh is often called upon to solve.

The electrical fixture market in Eldoret is increasingly dominated by Chinese plastic switch boxes, outlets, and plugs. They form a large portion of new installations and are even being sold by supermarkets. In the Philippines and Southeast Asia, these fixtures are sold by Chinese merchants who maintain control over all steps of the supply stream. In Eldoret, with no Chinese merchants, the Asian merchants supply the materials from a juncture of expertise and economic internationalism. Line voltage is translated into useful force through a nexus of knowledge and finance that happens to be ethnic.

Asians are "native strangers" in Kenya who render Kenyan-produced power useful to themselves and the Kenyan elite through imported appliances. They are a "middleman minority" in socioeconomic as well as technological terms. The Asians really are a disparate group of peoples representing regional cultures and religions at odds with each other in India. However, their common economic classification in Kenya has led to mutual action among former enemies. Like other middleman minorities, the Asians form similar associations on the basis of regional origins.

An example of this distant togetherness is the proximity of the Sikh temples and association buildings to the Hindu temples and social hall on Moi Avenue in Eldoret.

By providing fixtures and expertise, the Asians see that line voltage is formed and shaped for their own interiors. Kenya may have moved toward indigenizing the production of electricity, but the devices that transform it into useful work are imported, sold, and generally owned by Asians and foreigners.

8. The Fundi Complex

A *fundi*[1] is one who has learned a trade practice and can teach it to others, as opposed to a *mwalimu*, which refers to an educator, a schoolteacher, or a mosque teacher. ("Mwalimu" is a word that likewise stands at the center of a complex of its own.) Julius Nyerere, the former president of Tanzania, was referred to as "Mwalimu" by his followers. A number of Kenyan officials have adopted the title of "professor," whether they have an academic justification or not. None has suffered the title "fundi" to be attached to his name.

The word "expert" appears frequently in Kenyan English newspapers in association with gatherings at conferences and studies of national needs. It seems to be a way of merging "fundi" with "mwalimu" for the sake of contemporary emphasis on instrumentality and intellectual authority. There are *fundi wa viatu* (shoemakers), and *fundi wa magari* (mechanics), but no *fundi wa computer* (yet). There are computer experts.

The streets of Eldoret are lined with fundi. Most conspicuous are the men and women seated at treadle sewing machines, or men with their lasts and leatherworking patterns spread over cloths on the shaded part of the pavement. They seldom are alone. The sewing machines form lines, and the shoemaking materials are pooled among several men working in something like a circle. The fundi wa viatu, especially, may have a sideline: a spread of newspapers and magazines, a table with sweets, and paper cones of salted ground nuts, perhaps watched over by a child.

Some have tall stools where a customer can sit to have his shoes polished, encouraging the kind of sociability that the *kinyozi* (hairstyling) parlors provide for women. If not otherwise busy, the shoemakers-polishers can offer germane criticism of the shoes of passersby. There might be an orderly display of horseshoe-shaped metal taps they can add to shoes to reduce wear. The *fundi wa nguo,* or *washoni,* the men and women with the sewing machines, concentrate on that single line of mechanical work, though they display about them the brightly colored materials they can form into suits, dresses, uniforms, or even flags.

The work of these two most conspicuous types of fundi is both creation and repair, for the same reason that bicycle shops (with their own fundi) both build and reconstruct bicycles. Shoes and clothing are a large investment and must be maintained. The Asian-run clothing and shoe stores sell the new products of Indian, Chinese, Japanese, and Korean industries, but the prices are outside the range of all but the Asians themselves and the more affluent Kenyans. A few stores sell athletic chic running shoes and outfits at Euro-American prices. More affordable is the used clothing imported by the bale from overseas and, until early 1992, sold at a large outdoor clothing market across the street from the food market in the center of the town.

The street fundi can custom-fashion shoes and clothing at negotiable prices quite competitive with the ready-made materials, and they repair frayed seams and flapping soles to prolong the life of used articles. They also perform the alterations required to make the used clothes and shoes serviceable. The technology of these fundi can still replace and supplement mechanized production.

The limited Kenyan advertising industry[2] has not yet succeeded in cultivating a throwaway ethos in apparel and other goods. The socially insecure consumer (Ewen 1976) who regards purchasing used apparel as a sign of extreme destitution, and who has only limited tolerance for recycled goods, has yet to develop here.

The fundi who operate on the street either learned their skills by training with an established artisan or taking a course and passing an examination. Those who pass the Kenya Certificate of Primary Education examination can, with further training, sit for the artisan examination. Those with the Certificate of Secondary Education can, after preparation at a technical institute, sit for the craft examination and enter craft apprenticeships (building, electrical engineering, and manufacturing). The technical institutes, except for a specialized few such as the railway school, are under the aegis of the Ministry of Research, Technical Training, and Technology (now Ministry of Technical Training and Applied Technology), and the examinations are conducted by the National Examinations Council. Artisan skills, such as dressmaking and tailoring, and crafts, such as engineering and printing, are learned, certified, and deployed under both government and trade association regulations.

Geoffrey and Mutiso (1979:165) noted in their study of technical training in Kenya that the institutes then being developed

> can hardly be expected to do more in their curricula and syllabi than to reflect the demands of the existing political/economic structure. Which, in this case, are *not* for craftsmen and technicians skilled in improvising solutions to a wide range of technical problems but for people trained to service the products sold by or the machines used in a particular firm and to replace rather than repair when a difficulty arises. . . . The identity of interests of the political petty bourgeoisie and multi-national corporations in ensuring this outcome must be emphasized. Thus frustration rather than technicalization is the likely outcome.

They predicted that the institutes under these conditions would recruit students of elite parentage who couldn't make it in the academic system.

Though the national technical education system has been centralized and reorganized since Geoffrey and Mutiso's study, the development of the system has been much as they foresaw. In April 1993, for instance, the Kenya National Examinations Council sent circulars to the principals of the technical institutes informing them that 1,612 students of the institutes who had applied for the craft examination did not have the minimum requirements for entry into the examinations (a minimum aggregate grade of D+ in English and mathematics) and would have to sit for the lower-level artisan exam instead. The admission of these underqualified students into the technical institutes was attributed to "political manipulations" (*Nation*, 14 May 1993:1). This gross disqualification appears to have been the product of a political struggle between the ministry and the examinations council.

Geoffrey and Mutiso also noted that the majority of artisans on the street were without formal training. That continues to be true in Eldoret today, and increasingly so as artisans acquire their skills through informal apprenticeships and begin working independently as soon as they have the complement of tools. The difficulty of raising even primary school fees has strengthened informal training and made it subject to further attacks from established business and political interests.

Many formally trained artisans and craftspeople, notably welders and auto mechanics, work for large automotive, hardware, building supply, and electrical dealerships, often national chains such as Dobie-Cooper Motors or GEPS. The lines of division between formally trained/commercially employed and informally trained/self-employed artisans also reflect ethnic differences.

Patterns typical of the society also apply to the work of the fundi. Because of the strong prejudice against intentional physical contact between men and women in any public setting, there must be both male and female clothing fundi. There are no male fashion experts who fit dresses for women. The forced quarters of the bus or matatu, where women and men are in a proximity that would otherwise be regarded as immodest, simply underline the ability of culture to sustain categories that defy mechanical and economic necessity.

Deliberate contact is distinguished from necessary and accidental contact. The female clothing fundi has learned her skill as it applies to women, and she would not think of measuring a man for a suit, though she knows how to cut the pattern and piece it together. The brightly colored, flowery fabrics displayed behind her are suitable only for women's clothing; behind the male fundi, *wa nguo,* is darker cloth with subdued patterns for suits and trousers. ("Trousers" is an exclusive term in Kenyan English. "Pants," as some Americans learn to their chagrin, signifies "underwear" only, and the growing number of Kenyan women who wear trousers has increased the embarrassment of this language mistake.) A woman tailor shows neither the means nor the disposition to make men's clothing, and a male tailor is just as unlikely to make women's clothing. For either to suggest that they might would imply an interest in something other than the application of their skills.

Another important opposition is between the fundi and the unskilled person. Women and men may learn to sew up rents in garments, but they are unlikely to make clothes or undertake alterations or major repairs. They do not know how to use sewing machines unless that is their business and they have put time and money into training and equipment. The non-professional acquisition of specialized tailoring skills by men and women in Europe and America is not an option for most Kenyans. The availability of motorized and computerized sewing machines in the more affluent societies specifies a socioeconomic field of skill absent in Kenya.

Tailor with
Chinese-made treadle
machine

An old electric sewing machine that passed through Kenyan port customs was roughly pried apart with crowbar and screwdriver even though it could easily have been opened on hinges for inspection. The device was incomprehensible because although it resembled something familiar, its peculiar fitting and electrical cord gave it an air of possibly sinister purpose. The customs officials and warehouse thieves recognize fax machines and compact disk players with no trouble, but an electric sewing machine makes no sense to them because it is designed to fill a skill niche (home clothesmaking) that does not exist in their scheme of things. A clothing fundi would never need such a device. Who in the world could use it?

The fundi has skills with definite attributes, and the non-fundi (or the fundi of another skill) grasps those skills with an inevitability both cognitive and economic. The fundi's mode of skill is manual, and machines merely extend those manual skills. The electric sewing machine is a nonesuch because it introduces an energy (that unpredictable line current) that is not intrinsic to the hand or its extension.

Because fundi are economic beings, if electric sewing machines suddenly became affordable and the current to power them became available on the street, they would learn how to use them. The fundi and their customers are economic beings, and the introduction of devices so expensive to operate and maintain would erase the competitive advantage of the treadle sewing machine and one kind of adroit hand. Ready-mades might become a cheaper alternative.

Gandhi was shrewd enough an economic revolutionary to realize that masses of men and women spinning and weaving at home could overcome the juggernaut of mechanized mills in Britain because the colonists were dependent upon the Indian market to sell their goods. In Eldoret, with three large government-owned clothing mills providing employment nearby, the treadle sewing machine has a place because it and its operator are situated between home and factory. The hand has to touch the cloth in precisely a configuration that makes a product useful to the majority of people.

The fundi as a practitioner of handwork is a locus of training and of the economy. Even when his or her primary object is a machine, as with

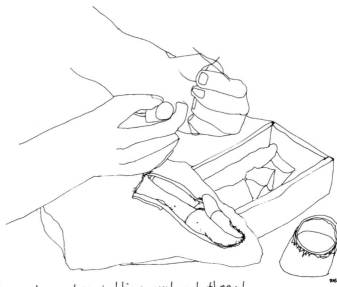

Hands of a shoemaker holding awl and thread

the auto mechanic, the hand itself is the center of the fundi's work. The work of individual fundi can only be treated as a manner of the hand that has been transmitted in learning the craft.

Watching Sara guide cloth, Otieno pierce leather, Dana cut hard rubber, or Sammy cut a key or guide a torch can reveal much about what technology reposes in the hand itself and how that comes with the training of the fundi. It is, of course, also a matter of a context of basic skills, built upon such assumptions as inertial balance. The exercise of the skill and the appearance of its product can easily seem to be the work of a formula endlessly and monotonously repeated, and thus uninteresting after the first description. Or it can be idealized like Ruskin's "shaping hand," which by its nature imposes an order upon the material. Remembering that this is a particular place and time and group of people, I will consider the work of different fundi in the culture of their manual address to different materials. The materials are the same everywhere—rubber is rubber, and metal is metal—but they possess qualities that make them singularly suitable to the livelihood operations of these fundi. The people meet the materials as fundi whose distinct purposes the materials must be made to reflect.

Fundi *wa kufuli*, "locksmiths," were not uncommon in Eldoret before the "cleansing" in the center. There were several in the central market and in tiny booths scattered in the artisan sections of town and in the jua kali area established near the river. The booths are hollow structures formed of wooden pieces nailed together, crossed by a wire from which are suspended lock and key blanks, perhaps a vise, and a sign such as "We cut key."

The work these fundi perform is the same as locksmiths everywhere: making copies of keys and opening intransigent locks. Eldoret does not yet have electric key-duplicating machines, so the manual reproduction of keys faces no competition from more efficient devices. The large trade in car and apartment keys and lock opening that locksmiths practice elsewhere is not so important. The masses of keys sported by men suggest that a key maker may have a role in building male identity. Though accumulation of keys contributes to display, the keys are originally each for a purpose, which is usually mail delivery and household security.

Kenya does not have home delivery of mail, so most people receive their letters through post office boxes. In major cities, postal centers are batteries of boxes, all of uniform size and distributed in exterior walls accessible to post office personnel from the inside. Eldoret has ten thousand numbered boxes including those at the main post office and a single smaller subsidiary at K Square on the industrial outskirts.

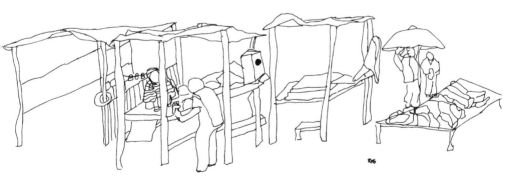

Outdoor kiosks with key maker and loudspeaker

The post office rents boxes to individuals annually and upon availability, usually after the previous tenant has defaulted in payment and the box has been locked by pulling a latch from the inside. When this happens, the post office is often unsuccessful in collecting the keys even though the previous tenant can no longer remove mail from the box. Often the procedure is to assign the box number to a new tenant who pays the fee and then is entitled to receive mail at that box number. However, because no key is available, the mail is given out at a delivery desk.

There is a natural tendency to share boxes, especially among urban families who have rural relations with no mail service. The system of hand delivery also lends itself it to delays and abuses that encourage people to maintain one common box. As more boxes in effect become closed through this system, more people share the same boxes, and each set of users requires a key. When a box is shared, a master key (one that works) is produced, and a copy is made for the new participants. The fundi wa kufuli makes the copy.

The Eldoret fundi who cut keys have reputations for accuracy and honesty, but seldom does a duplicate key work in the lock the first time. It is necessary to keep returning to the fundi for further attempts to match the copy to the lock. Fundi offer to go to the post office box in question and match the key, but it is considered unwise for the box user to give him that information. The only distinction between the user and anyone else is the knowledge where the particular key fits. The fundi's customers generally do not admit him to this knowledge. His work is mechanical and verified in a lock unknown to him. Customers, on the other hand, have been known to return to a fundi with other keys that they claim are unworking versions of one previously prepared by that fundi. This is where a fundi's memory of the configuration of keys serves him well.

· The fundi who is asked to copy a post office box key first has to find a blank corresponding to the original. These keys are standardized: a zinc-alloy round head with a hole at the far end from which a rod projects, supporting about halfway down its length a rectangular block of iron with the pattern. There are many patterns, all variations on the rectilinear cut and tooth that resembles a cluster of buildings. The dimensions of depth and length of cut and tooth are sufficient to provide for more than

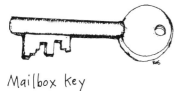

Mailbox Key

ten thousand mutually incompatible variations within the .2-by-.5-by-2-centimeter dimensions of the key block. Freely varying the number of cuts required within a one-millimeter dimensional tolerance will easily assure an absence of duplicate locks in a number as small as ten thousand.

A fundi reassured me that a working key to one box in Eldoret can be tried in all the others without a chance of a fit. That he knows this to be true in practice rather than merely theory demarcates a dimension of the fundi's knowledge. The same expert said that a good cutter can break any of the locks he chooses, but that it generally would not be profitable to do so, even in the long run, because mail is not so valuable and anything of worth is stolen in the post office before it ever arrives in the boxes. Breaking house locks is not profitable either because houses usually are otherwise guarded, and it is best to make a deal with the guard. A fundi can't make a living cutting keys, but he can add appreciably to his earnings if he gains a good reputation.

After receiving a master and finding the corresponding blank, the fundi mounts them side by side in a vise and begins to cut the blank to match the original. He uses a set of hard iron riffle files with coarse teeth for the rough cuts and smooth teeth for the finer cuts and finish work. The tools available and cutting styles vary from fundi to fundi, and there may be idiosyncrasies of certain training programs that did not appear because my sample was so small.

One fundi I observed attacked the deepest, most pronounced cut first. He drew the file along the blank's surface to establish a space of operations, compared it with the original, and commenced a sawing motion with the rough-toothed lower edge of his file. He continued this at an even pace, rocking in and out perhaps five centimeters on either side and bringing the body of the file into the established cut of the master. His strategy was to form the opening in the metal. In order to achieve the edge of the file needed for cutting all the way down, he had to angle the file as he drew it out toward himself on the side of the blank. The corners of the copy therefore flared where the original did not. Once he had rendered the depth of the first cut, the fundi started filing down a contiguous cut that formed a shelf above the first and shared its space into a widening. He was establishing the ensemble of spaces in the blank he was cutting to correspond with the original rather than aiming at an exact copy of the original.

The fundi had a functional reason for making a complete rough cut first (as diamond cutters do) and then taking to the finish work. He said that the copy is more likely to work if he can match the widths after the heights, since the locks work more from widths than heights. As he completed cutting the slots, the sawing motion became more separated into single strokes. He then removed the master from the vise and, laying it on the bench, checked it visually while he straightened the sides of the cuts with a light sanding motion to remove burrs and pockets.

The earlier concentration on the wholeness of the copy then gave way to what Chick and Roberts (1987), in their study of lathe work, call "part" appreciation. Examining the walls and outer surfaces of his cut for "smoothness," which he said would make the key look workable (*kufanyiza*) to the customer, the fundi gave the surfaces some expressive flourishes. When the key did not work, the fundi responded by finishing it more in comparison with the original. A fundi may take a key back and finish it without seeing the original again, even though the lock is far away.

Observations of other fundi at work suggest that their cognition of the key as a working part depends upon achieving a wholeness of a pattern that is then finished into a working state. If the fundi lacks access to the test of function—the lock—then he must create internal justifications of his skill and attempt to persuade the customer to accept them. The customer, as the fundi well knows, is intensely concerned with function, and thus the fundi is in a position different from the lathe operators, who often do not know what a part they make will be used for, or basket makers, whose craftsmanship does not face so exacting a functional test.

The fundi is dexterous, careful, and possessed of sound mechanical judgment, but his possession of these faculties is not in itself mechanical. He is not a machine. His use of his hands is guided conceptually and measured expressively. His social relation with a customer fills the gap between form and function, and he concentrates on fulfilling that relation, always hoping that his expressive solution to functional problems will be more of a shared value than the rigid criterion of whether or not the key turns in the lock.

The fundi's role as an instructor of his work begins to become clear in this account of the fundi wa kifuli. He shows the customer intent upon only one thing, a working key, what a key is. This may be the usual anthropological fallacy of idealizing the informant to the detriment of others in his vicinity. The fundi does not propose to accomplish this; it is the most gratifying way for him to conduct his business. The ability to envelop his craft in mystique, except for highly specialized workers such as escape artists and safecrackers, is less pronounced than with the fundi of more complex mechanisms such as auto mechanics. The fundi wa kifuli does not require an expensive toolkit or a large fixed shop. He is closer to the fundi wa viatu, the shoemakers, and the fundi *wa tendo*, the rubber stamp makers, than to the sewing machine experts. But do these other fundi exercise their expertise similarly?

The stamp makers are as common as the key cutters on the streets of Eldoret. They also serve a need for copies, only in this case it is a need for originals from which copies are made. The bureaucratic commonplace of being in control of a stamp is as widespread in Kenya as in any other country with a large civil service. Banks and other organizations whose employees model themselves after the civil service also require the stamp makers' products. Here it is a matter of fixing a name, either a personal name or more likely the name of an office, in a hard rubber surface.

The stamp maker has a few standard models, a small repertoire of stamps that are considered of appropriate dignity. The fundi displays their impresses on a white sheet at his desk. The favored round or oval stamp requires deft maneuvering of the fundi's knife to form the letters distributed about the curve. The customer gives him a text and selects a stamp blank in the preferred size and shape. There might even be an older, worn stamp to copy.

Unlike the key cutter, this fundi faces an immediate test of the efficacy of his work in the impress shown to the customer. The test is not as exacting as the key fit into the lock, and the fundi is more likely to develop an attitude of concurrence with the customer's wishes and gauge his craftsmanship accordingly. Office requirements can actually be narrower than the functional requirements of the key in lock. One narrow range of stamp forms is considered official and maintains that status for a long time.

If the rubber stamp fundi has little space for expressive play, the welder (*fundi wa unganisha*) may have too much. His work is similar to that of the cloth workers both in the kind of work performed and in the tools required. Like the tailors and dressmakers, the welder forms new objects and repairs or alters old ones by cutting and joining solid materials. The welder uses a torch, while the cloth workers use needle and thread or sewing machine. The manual skills required by the welder, who also learns his trade in a polytechnic or commercial school, are very different from those of any other fundi because of the nature of the materials he works with and the temper of his tool.

Many of the street fundi informally associate into groups based on common language and place of origin. Welders are likely to be associated with other types of workers rather than with other welders, and they may practice other skills, such as metal beating or auto repair, in association with their welding work. They use an oxyacetylene torch fed by two metal cylinders held in a carriage, and a 50- to 60-hertz electric arc transformer, also portable. The two outfits complement each other well in the welder's work, the oxyacetylene used for cutting and soft joining, the arc for working heavy steel.

Welding House is a tiny shop not too far from the entrance to an alley that extends parallel to the main road. Three men work there, all qualified as welders but tending to specialize in different jobs, and all of them Kikuyu by origin. Crammed into their space are several torch outfits, an electric arc, and a submerged head welding bed for plate jobs. The welders

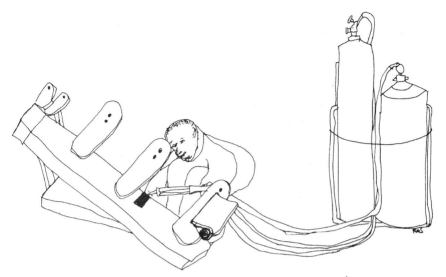

Welder fabricating mount beam for a disk harrow

engage in both fabrication and repair, and they not only work at the shop but also have portable equipment. A typical welding job is constructing security barriers for shop doors and windows. All of the shops in Eldoret have such barriers, and the stores with more portable, more desirable goods—consumer electronics and liquor—are fortresses of thick bars fixed onto girder frames.

Forming impassable configurations of security bars accounts for much of the welders' business. For domestic settings, the bars can be made attractive, and ready-made window barriers are displayed in jua kali areas. Commercial shields, on the other hand, must look impassable, and one welder named James built a shop front so formidable that it is known as "the black rhino."

After receiving a commission to strengthen the shell over a shop door in the post office row, James brought both types of welding outfit and a metal beam the same size as the others that crossed the frame. The merchant was worried that the existing bars were too far apart, and he wanted James to add two more. James knew that this would be spot-welding work and brought a supply of the right iron-tin flux. He checked the beam to make certain of the fit and then found a hookup for the arc inside the shop.

James worked beside the line of passing pedestrians using a hand-held shield before his face. Holding the beam flush to the frame with a wire at one end, he wedged a pellet of flux between the frame and the beam and, with the ground clip fixed on the cross member of the frame, brought the cleaned electrode toward a point on the frame just above the pellet. When the electrode was close enough to form an arc, James used a downward zigzagging motion to liquify the pellet. The beam came into the liquid just as he withdrew the arc. Moving to the two other places where spots had to be joined, he pressed in pellets that were there and retired the arc. He completed the job with the oxyacetylene torch, melting flux into the open joints and brazing off any rough areas on the metal.

All of James's work on this project was systematic and clearly programmed by the instruction he had received in school, even to the manner of moving the arc in the vicinity of the seam. Yet he clearly had an overall idea of how his work should look: the regular melt of the bond, the smooth and straight course of the finish. While he never lost sight of the objective—fastening the cross pieces to the frame—he clearly was welding rather than just fastening. The program of the act exceeded the outcome. The expressive element came in obedience to the program, which was the only way to contain the force required. Those of us looking from the outside and seeing the unique creative act of welding probably don't appreciate how boring it is when the arc follows its pool hour after hour over meters of security frames.

The men at Welding House also fabricate jiko that are sold in the market, and metal cases that are sold at a shop on Moi Avenue, on the other side of the alley. Both require cutting sheet metal as well as hammering.

The jiko are metal drums about one-quarter meter in diameter that are fitted with prongs on the top rim to hold the screen, three tall legs on the bottom, and a pair of metal handles curving far out from the body. A small opening is cut in the base, and a piece of metal with a handle is fixed to a pivot that allows it to slide over the opening and serve as an air regulator. All of these pieces are cut from scrap using an arc or saw and affixed to the body with a torch.

The cases are formed of pieces of sheet metal, often taken from auto bodies, cut into rectangles of the appropriate size with triangles cut where there will be seams. The side walls are then formed by hammering, and the seams are welded shut. Also welded onto the cases are a hinged lid, handles, and a clasp. The cases are a very inexpensive means of conveying goods: a case 2-by-1-by-2 meters costs about five hundred shillings (a little more than six dollars). I saw them for sale in an American "ecological" gift catalogue for fifty to one hundred dollars.

The people who need to draw upon ever recycled materials frequently resort to using welders in the technical realm of Eldoret. The welders can join together pieces of scrap metal to make standard appliances, and they know how to improvise replacement auto parts that are not available or are too expensive. (The techniques they employ in making these adjustments are worthy of a separate treatise, but in this case, such an undertaking might draw too much attention to the generally mechanical, and away from the specific of technology in Eldoret.)

Because welding is used for the same purposes everywhere it is a recognized skill, to identify seeming peculiarities in Eldoret might commit the fallacy of overspecifying the universal. The same might be said of other skills associated with auto-refitting, cylinder boring, and metal lathe work, which may be practiced idiosyncratically but never so uniquely that they fail to meet the bore tolerances of the pistons. The specialists in these skills are fundi constrained by the mechanism, and they practice their skills accordingly.

While fundi as "masters" of artisanship are largely a product of the polytechnic and trade schools, which tend to define and consolidate their crafts, they also are defined as specialists in certain materials, and their tools simply enable them to manipulate these materials. There are several types of fundi for each material subject to fashioning and refashioning: wood, metal, stone, rubber, and paper. Some types of fundi are easily ignored because they are defined more by a material they obtain and form than by a specific title or textbook skill.

For instance, although they are not categorized as such, there are "tire fundi." Tubeless tires, which cannot readily be repaired, have not become the standard in Kenya, so far sparing the country the enormous used-tire disposal problem that forms part of the waste disposal agony in other parts of the world. Instead, tires are used and reused until there is very little left of them. When tires are no longer roadworthy—and this means exposure of the fabric bands—men skilled at the practice cut them into pieces for sale to shoemakers, who use them as sole components or shape them into parts and objects. (One sandal maker who migrated from Uganda uses tire rubber to make entire sandals, and he displays them by sticking them between the wires of a chain-link fence that fronts the "lower" bus park beside the river.)

Working with vulcanized rubber is a "subtractive" rather than an "additive" craft (Vansina 1984:61) like metalworking: the finished product must always be less in volume than the original, as well as constrained in shape by the original. Given these limitations, some of the work with tire bodies is sculptural. Fundi manage to cut secants out of three-meter

Boy rolling a tractor tire

truck tires to form water cradles where inner tubes can be checked for leaks. They also pull the embedded wire out of expended tires and sell that to a separate set of fundi, who use it to make rat traps.

Complex devices that require a number of fittings made of different materials are often addressed by fundi who have the most experience with those materials. The upholstery of automobiles is now the work of tailors; the body the province of metalworkers and welders. Some pieces do not clearly fall into anyone's bailiwick and have to be assigned on the basis of facility with that general form and material.

The visors of cars and trucks wear out rapidly in the equatorial sun and must be replaced. Unlike many motor parts, they cannot be easily adapted from one model to another; new visors have to be made. The making of visors has fallen into the hands of sign makers because they often handle the masonite and thin fiberboard used as the base of signs, and they also cut coverings for the signs. They can flatten rectangles of masonite, shape the visors, and face them with black oilcloth, then fit them with tubular rods to accept the visor posts, as they might a hanging sign. None of this has to do with the sign maker's main skill, which is painting the letters and figures of the sign on the board or wall surface (see chapter 13).

All of the fundi adapt existing skills to new forms and materials if it proves profitable to them. This happens most often when someone needs a part that no one has learned to manufacture. There is a great deal to be learned about the adaptability of a fundi's skills, and the cognition that encompasses their exercise, from looking at their role in refitting broken-down machinery. The project of automobile repair often includes several fundi (welding, metalworking, rubberworking, key cutting) besides the mechanic himself. Reconstruction of a plow or a disk harrow begins with welders but then passes to metalworkers and others.

It seems that new fundi do not come about as easily as old fundi learn to master new forms of expertise. The xerox machine has proliferated in Eldoret over the last decade in proportion to the proliferation of government and commercial copying. At the very least, an individual has reasons to copy his or her national identity card and school or training certificates. The maintenance and repair of the machines is still mostly in the hands of a small cadre of technicians employed by the manufacturers (Gestetner and Xerox). They are not fundi but experts. The operation of the machines, however, has fallen to employees of the stores where the service is available. No customer is allowed to make his or her own copies. The operator, or xerox fundi, must work the machine. This is due in part to the large investment the machine represents: only a trusted employee should be allowed to handle it. It also is due to the xerox expertise this employee has developed. She or he (most often she) knows how to fit the maximum within the copying surface of the machine without losing lines, how to copy both sides of an identity card, cut them out, and paste them back to back in order to form an identical copy, and how to do all of this quickly.

These are not trivial skills in a trade as competitive as the xerox business. The machines are lodged in bookstores, office supply stores, dry cleaning establishments, and general merchandise stores. One machine is lodged inside a wood-framed glass cube like those favored by watch repairers, with a young woman, seated, operating it. Because people know where the best prices and the best copies are to be had, the designated xerox fundi of each establishment must be up to the demands of the public.

Competition acts as a control on all of the fundi and assures a continual shakedown in each of the practices. The frailest trades are those that require the least capital and the most moveable tools. Locksmiths and shoemakers have come and gone over a two-year period, but tailors, welders, and garage mechanics have tended to remain. Itinerant craftspeople—a doll maker and a maker of basket-like traps for rats—fashion their works on the spot, sell them, and then move on.

All of these trades are ephemeral because they are not fixed by buildings and institutions but only by the general level of service they provide. They are highly vulnerable to obsolescence through the arrival of machines and types of goods that can replace their handicrafts at a lower price level. Key-cutting machines in a few of the hardware stores would reduce but not entirely eliminate key-cutting fundi. Inexpensive ready-made garments or the reduction of the used clothing market would seriously curtail the work of the tailors. Mechanics and welders are less vulnerable, though they might face absorption by the institution of garages and shops. Many of the fundi practice independently or, at most, cooperatively. The existing teamwork can be mechanized and institutionalized when that becomes economically more efficient. The technology is then altered.

Another pressure to which the individual and loosely teamed fundi are susceptible is government regulation, which seems to run in tandem with the changing economic currents that bring technological shifts. In recent years, a growing municipal perception of the fundi practicing in the downtown is that they are extraneous clutter hampering the flow of life and business. The fundi, both individuals and shops, have tended to cluster in certain areas: the tailors along the streets where they can shelter under the overhangs; the shoemakers wherever there is a flow of pedestrian traffic. As the municipality has evolved a physical identity, it has increasingly moved to order and then to exclude technologies that are not used within confined spaces and under the direct governance of heavily capitalized economic formation.

The fundi complex is best summarized as a manual engine for the transformation of materials, to keep in use what cannot be made anew by recycling and restoring. Fundi provide for the materials and finished product manufacturing that do not exist in Kenya. Theirs is a male sector of technology because women have not been admitted into their training until very recently and because women's work is not defined as fundi work. The cities offer the greatest opportunities for men (but not women) who want to learn technical skills. The materials are available, and the market is always open to low-cost products. However, growing cities like Eldoret are increasingly unfriendly to fundi, who escape formal economic and educational controls and represent "unruly" social elements trying to participate in an economic milieu irregularly technologized.

9. Teamwork and Management

Occasionally a group of people will push a disabled vehicle to the crest of a hill in Eldoret and then hop in as it begins to roll downhill. The theory is that the vehicle, once rolling, will resume its own motive force and continue. Several of the garages operate towing or "recovery" services, but they are expensive and predicated upon there being something to tow. However, the exhausted matatu or pickup truck may need to keep going because its margin of profitable operation will not allow any other outcome. Thus when a machine fails, the muscles of the operators or passengers are called on and often determine whether the outcome is inaction or continued service. Due to the nature of the mode of transport, everyone on a stranded matatu stands to lose if it is not made operational as quickly and simply as possible. This calls for a spontaneous teamwork unlike the cooperation of kin mates or regular workmates, a supplementary enabling of technology through harnessing group order.

Mechanized technology in Eldoret often calls for human replacement of failed energy sources. The amount of energy required to move a mass the size of a disabled vehicle means that another external powerplant must be brought into play. The scarcity of powerplants of all kinds, which is why the machines are so overused that they fail, demands animal or human replacement. The donkey and the ox, the main Kenyan draft animals, are uncommon in urban areas; humans are the only alternative power available. But humans must work together to achieve the cumulative impetus, which means abandoning passive passenger, consumer, or observer roles and joining hands to the effort.

An agrarian or pastoral livelihood (with its customary joint physical exertion to a readily visible end) and the frequency of accidents and breakdowns contribute to assuring that teams form as needed and disband once the task is done. A pastoral background also provides a means of communication among members of a team used to locating other herders in a bushy area, or signaling someone across a planted field.[1] If a truck needs pushing, or an overturned hulk must be lifted off someone pinned beneath it, the task is swiftly accomplished.

When a six-wheel flatbed truck would not start up outside the grain warehouse where it had made a delivery, it was taken in hand by a group of eight men: the driver and his "shift boy," two workers from the warehouse, and four passersby who saw the need and volunteered. The task was to push the truck about fifty meters down a side road, up a slope onto the main road, and into traffic down the grade.

The driver entered the cab, and the men positioned themselves four at the back, two on one side, and one on the other. The driver released the emergency brake and called to the shift boy, who put his shoulder to the

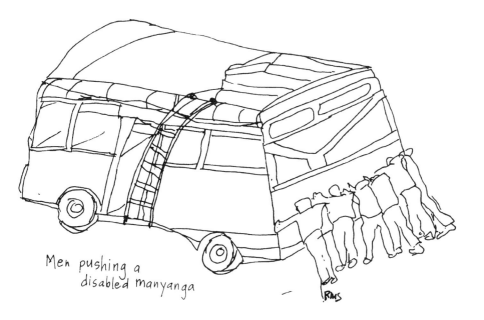

Men pushing a
disabled manyanga

RMS

rear of the rig, which the other men imitated, the three of them pressing to give the body a little motion on the flat road surface. Feeling the movement, the others began to push with their hands, and as the travel increased, they lay into the effort more firmly. The truck continued at a uniform walking pace to the edge of the main road, where the resistance of the slope slowed it. The driver began to turn the truck to the right, toward the left side of the main road, and nosing it out, gained the co-operation of oncoming traffic on the right, which halted.

As the crew was encountering the resistance of the truck trailer making the grade, they mutually increased their push in a spontaneous common response. The one man who was applying himself on the right shifted left to bunch with the men at the rear, and they concentrated to the left as the truck, now vectored by its wheels, turned in that direction. The array of force corresponded to the flux of inertia, and the men were lined against the gate in their effort. The truck began to rise up the slope as it turned. The decreasing effort demand caused one man at the left and then another to leave off pushing. It was only then that anyone spoke, and that was just to say, "This is done, I am going." The shift boy ran to enter the cab as the truck started down the road.

Teams might form and respond to each other in many different ways. They might give an appearance of greater cordiality, or of a remoteness from personal contact that might even verge on hostility apart from the dedication to effort. The lack of apparent supervision keeps a consciousness of the who and what of the task from becoming explicit, and keeps foremost the need for a level of output. Pushing a truck is a communal effort. Supervision, with its assignments and evaluations, injects the identities of the participants into the work, and the explicitly social enters the basically technological. A complex, engineered multiphase task, which has no singly changing wave of mechanical resistance to govern the participants, calls for supervision as well. But the supervised team performing a simple task is divorced from the simple common drive and must accomplish a task of outward-looking solidarity as well as the job at hand.

This sounds like the social science argument of organic versus mechanical solidarity, where the spontaneous group response to a mechanism in need of energy is "organic" while the supervised response is "mechanical." A developing tradition of labor and industrial sociology has grounded this distinction in work patterns. The matatu passengers who push their vehicle over the hill are an organic team, whereas the workers who stand in a drainage pit, shovels in hand, listening to the instructions of a water department official standing above are at that moment a mechanical team.

If this distinction is to be made, it should be recognized that the organic solidarity of such teams is narrow, conditional, and specifically functional, while the mechanical solidarity is broad, general, and multifunctional. The organic team forms in a moment, does its work, and is done; the mechanical team is formed on a basis unrelated to a specific task and is available for a range of orders. The organic team exists as a set of passengers, passersby, onlookers, or acquaintances; the mechanical team has its basis in a class, a set of relatives, a tribe, or a club. Supervision is provided on the same basis as direction in any of these other organizations. The supervisor is the father, the elder, the chief, or the member of the next age set. The organic/mechanical distinction in the study of task and management is not a rigid and absolute distinction, but it does help to envision the connections and analogues of team conduct and management systematics in a variety of situations.

When a pickup truck piled with sacks of fertilizer concentrate arrives at an agricultural supply store, a team forms to unload it. The supervision comes from the driver, who decides how close he can bring the truck to the entrance of the store, and from the proprietor, who says he wants the sacks laid on the sidewalk. The sidewalk in this part of town is a raised cement pier planted with concrete posts to support the shading overhang. After the driver has backed the truck as close as he can, the driver's assistant (not in this case a "shift boy" because he does not drive) stands in the bed of the truck and raises one of the twenty-kilogram bags. He tosses it about two meters to a shop worker standing beside the high raised pier of the sidewalk. The worker catches it and hands it up to another shop worker standing where the sacks are to be positioned. The relay continues, with sacks passing at regular intervals until they are all laid neatly on the sidewalk awaiting further disposition. The mechanical unit formed at first between the driver and the shopkeeper gives way to an organic unit based upon muscular coordination and balance to create the completed position and order. This accomplished, the team breaks up with few words to each other. Although it is certainly conceivable that this kind of relay could be organized among any group of people who would need this task accomplished, it is obvious that a common ground of inertial balance and muscular timing have combined to give this teamwork its outward form.

If there were a mechanized delivery system with conveyor belt and forklifts, and a building design that permitted easy access to storage spaces (a technology increasingly visible in Eldoret), then this team would not come about. It is a human technology that arises out of existing capacities and is replaced only when the increased scale of operations calls for machines able to move larger loads into place more efficiently. It is a sad development in Africa that the machinery is sometimes introduced before the volume handled makes it more efficient than muscle power. The workers are idled and so, perhaps, are the machines when the need fluctuates or prices rise. Or bureaucratic chicanery in effect makes the storage facilities useless, as at the government maize storage complex in Eldoret, which was reported full but found to be empty when the need for maize became severe.

A contrast with the teamwork of pushing vehicles and unloading sacks is the competitive but ultimately cooperative process of fruit and vegetable delivery and display. This involves the technological transformation of plant life into collections ordered for sale by individuals. Two intersecting types of teamwork accomplish this: the commodity stream that secures, packs, transports, and delivers the produce, and the selling agency that makes it available to the buying public. The public encounters all stages of this teamwork but pays attention only to the final appearance.

There are in Kenya some rather conspicuous sales displays of produce; for instance, the stacked stone pillars that support bags of oranges in a forested area on the Nairobi road outside Gilgil, and the large pyramids of the Kisumu indoor market. The Eldoret market and street sellers of fruit and vegetables most often spread out their wares, though some make small heaps or arrangements. The stone pillars are used by maize roasters on the streets.

Potatoes are a good illustration of arrangement work. They are grown in the Eldoret area but are farmed in greater volume farther downslope near Timboroa and Londiani. Groups of women unearth and wash them, then pack them in bags for shipment to a potato and cabbage market at the main bus stop about fifteen kilometers from Timboroa town. The market's style of display is worth noting because it is transferred more or less intact to the sale of potatoes in Eldoret municipal market.

The large bags arrive by truck or slung over the backs of donkeys. Usually it is women who drive and unload the donkeys, men who load, drive, and unload the trucks. The women, though competing with each other, cooperate in getting the large bags from the delivery point to the selling area, which is very near the road. The women wash the potatoes and place them in two-liter margarine cans. These displays are arrayed in a row at the roadside. When a customer—any bus, matatu, or private car—comes to a halt nearby, the women rush with their sacks to the doors and windows. They invariably ask the same price for potatoes that are to all appearances identical, and though selecting one woman to bargain with may lead to a lower price, there is usually very little deviation from the initial asking price. The women work together to maintain the price of the vegetables while competing to win this or that particular sale. The seeming uniformity of goods, measure, and display is apparently to

Women selling potatoes
near Timboroa, Nairobi Road

RMS

the advantage of the collectivity since no one seller can gain the edge. It is cooperative competition, another variety of teamwork.

In the Eldoret municipal market, potatoes are generally segregated from other fresh produce. The delivery and display are the same as at the bus stop, though it is not possible for the women to approach stopping vehicles as they do on the road. As exhibited in their cans lining the curb of the roofed area, the potatoes are still a dramatic end point of a team process and evidence of a conformist struggle for sales. In the market, the same pieces, of the same quality, in the same condition, for the same prices, are offered on table after table. This competitive teamwork to control the discouragements of competition and keep prices within an acceptable range is common to all Kenyan small-scale selling operations and is in marked contrast to the conscious efforts of sellers in European and American markets to offer noticeably different wares. Rather than a single large monopolistic operator distributing the bulk of an item within an area, many small sellers duplicate each other and vary the sameness slightly by forming personal relationships with habitual purchasers or planning some small refinement of supply. This in turn limits the use of massive technology in packaging, display, and even in transport. The hawkers (for example, the cassette tape sellers discussed previously) who carry their wares or try to construct their minute wooden booths wherever they can are the strongest expression of this matrix of supply and teamwork. A yet more complex level is where artisans form shops in the same condition of competition and cooperate on a collective level.

A major organization for cooperative use of technology in Kenya is *jua kali* artisanship. "Jua" means "sun," and "kali" is "fierce," "the fierce, or full, sun." An English equivalent might be "open air" in the sense of an "open air market"; the French might be *plein air*, which adds a context of casual activities not entirely foreign to the social meaning of "jua kali." Jua kali artisans—most of whom are metalworkers, mechanics, and carpenters—are fundi, possibly with trade school backgrounds, who have organized themselves into shops under a countrywide label and with a national organization.

Each small village has its jua kali section, which is signposted as such. In the larger cities, these small shops are distinguished and physically set off from the large machine shops and garages often owned by Asians or Europeans, though staffed by Kenyans. In Eldoret, the distinction is quite visible. One of the large concentrations of jua kali shops is directly across from a concentration of heavy machine works. The theory that the informal sector provides a labor reserve for the formal sector comes to mind (Bromley and Gerry 1979), especially with any protracted observation of jua kali operations. Artisans from the small shops may find temporary jobs or take out work from the large ones and may, on the other hand, use the heavy equipment in the large shops more or less on the sly.

The jua kali shops operate with coordinated teamwork among cooperating artisans with different skills and connections. One or two fundi form the core of most shops, which may have a very modest plank-constructed shed or none at all. Any building is used for storage, to lock up materials or work. The construction activity goes on outside and has three phases: procurement of raw materials, work, and selling and delivery. No shop is large enough to vest any one of these entirely in an individual. The intersecting circle of teamwork in jua kali—like different people pushing different parts of the truck, but all pushing—develops through the connections of each of the artisans in the shop, and in the coordination of these connections to form a team.

Jua kali carpentry shops exist in all of the artisan areas of Eldoret. Actually, like the welding and machine shops, they are one form in a continuum that ranges from the single workman carpenter who has no particular locus, to large workshops outfitted with expensive stationary power tools and subsidized by entrepreneurs who know little of carpentry. Their products are as consistent as the metalworking shops, only they are not as likely to make use of recycled materials. Beds, tables, and chairs of uniform design are constructed from local hardwoods and then finished and delivered to the commissioning customer.

The wood for a bed is procured from a lumber supplier—there are three major ones in Eldoret—in the quantity required for the project. Lumber is not supplied dimensionally but is available in rough-cut logs, which the lumber merchant then cuts into boards of requested size. The outer bark and sawdust are also sold, the former to serve as the outer skin of huts, and the latter to brewers, tanners, or gardeners. The furniture-

Men standing outside a furniture shop
where fundi work

RnS

making operation will consist of hand-cutting the four pieces of the bed
frame, the legs, the cross planks to support the mattress, and further
pieces and pegs for a small head piece. The artisans work as a team to assure uniformity of the result in the absence of power tools. The structure
of this teamwork varies from one shop to another: the team is a device
for obtaining conformity to a commonly expected form. Power equipment simply speeds, and makes mechanical, the cooperation that is already possible in its absence. The aim is a bed that resembles all other
beds and meets standards of stability and finish.

A task-oriented team is a group whose members have common backgrounds and work toward common ends embodied in a form with a social
necessity they all perceive. Thus when Muangi applies a coat of finish to
the bed, he is bringing a shared work that much closer to delivery. He
formed the pegs for the bed head and attached the legs to the cross pieces
because his partner was drilling the holes for the pegs or cutting the cross
planks at the time. Teamwork here is cognition of the uniform whole that
implies cognition of the coordinated parts. One does not drill holes into a
piece that someone else is trying to cut—which is an absurd example, but

refine it greatly and the quality of cooperation becomes more clear. Constructing a piece of furniture is not a narrative as making a key might be; it is a state of relations between individuals who are members of distinct groups. This state of relations shows itself in an object that is well assembled. Members of shops belong to the same political party, speak the same vernacular language, marry from the same village, went to the same polytechnic, and so on. The finished bed is part of this list. Members of other shops who belong to different political parties, etc., make the same bed.

The jua kali sector of the economy is problematic in Kenyan culture because of the kind of teamwork that makes its producers the producers they are. They do not seem capable of the collective action that matatu touts and hawkers exhibit, at least in the larger cities. At a symposium accompanying the Western Province jua kali exhibition in Kakamega on 4 November 1992, Mr. James Bwatuti, the chairman of the Kenya National Federation of jua kali associations, complained that seven and a half acres of land set aside for jua kali sheds in Eldoret had been "grabbed" by politicians (*Nation*, 6 November 1992). Accusations of land grabs are common in Kenyan politics, and as in this case, the grabbers usually go unnamed or are said to be "influential people." Mr. Bwatuti may have been trying to force the surrender of land promised but not delivered, or attempting to consolidate his own position by speaking for his Eldoret constituents at an event in nearby Kakamega. He appealed to the government Ministry of Technical Training and Applied Technology "to resolve the dispute which had cropped up between the Eldoret District Commissioner's office and the local *Jua Kali* Association." Mr. Bwatuti was a government-appointed head of a union attempting to align his members with the government by seeking a redress from another government official. This is a strategy for bringing independent tradesmen under control within the jua kali designation. Some of the contested land finally was allocated to the hawkers and artisans, but only after they were ejected from the central market and forced to relocate all over town.

Several months earlier, hawkers in Nairobi had invaded the hotel room where the head of their national association was staying and "frogmarched" him to the police station, requesting that he be arrested for misappropriating funds. The hapless "boss" was granted police protection against further expressions of discontent by his constituents. This episode demonstrated a degree of teamwork not usually expected among competitive sellers like hawkers. Clearly their boss was no consensual King of the Hawkers, but a businessman and political appointee like many other union heads. His shaming was due to the inconsistency of a fancy hotel room with the state of his assigned followers. He never would have thought of interrupting a presidential pageant with an onslaught of hawkers in order to force a response to their demands. For the hawkers, the teamwork potential in the background of everyone on their economic level has become a basis for urban group action. Hawkers also demand land to construct booths, but they put forward those demands vehemently, may take the land by force, and battle with police sent to evict them.

Artisans may also behave this way, but their investment in equipment that can be confiscated and the contractual nature of their work seem to make them less mobile than hawkers, who sell what they can carry. At the same jua kali exhibition, much attention was given to the difficulty artisans have obtaining adequate bank loans to expand their operations and find outlets for their work in competition with imports and mechanized producers. Artisans who had built sheds on land near the Mathare valley, Nairobi (to select one among many examples), responded violently when police began to demolish the buildings (*Nation*, 13 November 1992).

Urban authorities object to structures they have not permitted and cannot regulate. Both private owners and municipal authorities treat urban land as an investment that they do not want devalued by kiosks and shops. The economic common ground between hawkers and artisans inspires similar responses to similar assaults. When the grand demolitions of artisan and hawker sheds came in Eldoret and Nakuru in early 1993 (chapter 14), they protested together and relocated together.

Leadership in a shopcraft setting is usually associated with management, with achieving such a degree of control over the means of production that the artisan becomes a manager from within. Artisans resemble women as economic actors in being unable to gain enough capital to make the transition "across the street" to forming large industrial shops. As with the domestic work of women, merely trying to run a household or a shop as it always has been leads to impoverishment as materials increase in cost. Artisan teamwork does not lend itself to wage labor. Associations are formed from above, and politicians assert hegemony by appointing bosses to head them. The artisans cannot make more and cheaper beds to maintain their status.

In this setting, with teamwork itself politicized and rendered into a class relationship with other types of production, the artisans have still managed to avoid becoming wage laborers or political hacks. The level on which they resist complete transformation is one more relationship vested in the technology of their operations. It has to do with the un-managed supply of parts and materials to their endeavors.

Because the craftsmanship is not wholly mechanized, the parts required are not rigidly specialized but can be as simple as a saw blade or a tanged head. There are hardware stores and even specialized woodworking suppliers. A large number of basic parts and tools are offered by street hawkers and other artisans. It is not unusual to see a hawker walking with a handful of screwdrivers and hacksaw blades. Although the ascending levels of artisan organization do not provide teamwork on the level of the town, region, or nation, the network of parts supply does offer the rudiments of inter-shop cooperation.

The auto/truck parts supply shows this even more emphatically. Several parts supply stores in Eldoret are owned by Asians who are quite conversant with formal sources and often able to manufacture or modify a part to specifications with machine tools they keep on the premises. N. M. Tailor, the owner of Eldoret Auto Spares, one of the oldest of these stores (1975), operates his own rubber-casting factory to provide elusive pieces. Each day he answers numerous queries about clutch plates, washers, bushings, and hoses, and he supervises a staff of Kenyan employees in the work of providing suitable replacements.

In effect, Tailor manages a parts business that formalizes what goes on much less formally in the wider world. The jua kali mechanics who come to him in search of matching parts have already tried other sources—

Men repairing a log-carrying
flatbed truck

mechanics in other shops and recyclers of metal who may have come
across the piece. A rank of specialists has developed who carefully and
ingeniously seek out a single part and who are the first resort of anyone
requiring a truck ignition solenoid or a platinum diesel injector. For
example, one man sits beneath the overhang of a detached truck trailer
the whole day long with an array of truck carburetor rings on a table before him. He has found the saddle point of demand and price for this
item, both receiving and providing, that allows him to maintain himself
and be a member of the fraternity of mechanics at the same time.[2] He is
not a storekeeper or a manager of supplies like Tailor. The teamwork of
parts provision has many inflections, but its participants know where formality and management begin. They cooperate loosely and effectively to
perpetuate teamwork that does not accede to management.

Construction is one major activity in Eldoret where intrinsic capacities for teamwork and management are destined to meet. Stonesmasons,
carpenters, metalworkers, other fundi, and day laborers are brought together for the completion of projects that are not fully the work of any
one trade, which means there must be a managerial presence that does
not emerge from among them and is not the political control of the

bosses. The gap between management and teamwork may be a reason for the enforced cooperation among artisans of different skills.

Construction supervisors are often members of outsider communities, Asian or European, which enables them to impose a degree of overall coordination upon the teamwork of the separate shopmates. Kenya has developed a class of professional technocrats who can accomplish this as well, though their ethnic identity is often tested by the workers, and they in turn test the workers' identity.

Eldo Supermarket at Eldo Center, a plaza of shops beside the post office downtown, began an expansion into an alcove outside its windows. The Sikh contractor hired by the Asian owner of the store set the tasks for the six Kenyan workers he employed. Workers drained and removed a goldfish pond that was in the square before the expansion. A carpenter built scaffolding extending from one wall to the other, and a walkway where two plasterers could stand as they coated the ceiling and upper walls with hydraulic cement. At the same time, two other masons built up the floor of the plaza to meet the elevated edges on the opposite sides.

After inspecting the site each morning, the contractor would order the required materials and tell the workers what they should accomplish that day. The contractor's idea of the project was to put as much work as possible into single tasks employing one type of material. This was to take maximum advantage of the workers' tendency to perform better when together on the same task, and the need to arrange delivery of cement and to monitor use. He had calculated into the cost of the project the total amount of cement required to cover the walls and ceiling to the desired thickness, and he allotted the amount needed for each day's work. The plasterers then had to cover a set area with what they were given; the same for the flooring masons.

The contractor therefore translated the teamwork of the fundi into the economics of his own operation. They were working together to finish a set labor with a fixed amount of material. This gave the work closure for the fundi, who were not performing all the labor to complete an object. They contributed as distinct teams to the contractor's business, which had a whole shape obscure to them. The contractor himself suggested that the workers' innumeracy would limit their ability to supervise the entire project. Included in the contractor's conception of numeracy, or capacity for quantitative thought, was also a shrewd management of the factors contributing to his own profit. Were the fundi similarly capitalized, they also could have performed the contractor's job. And they might. Although it is common for Kenyans to be the laborers and Asians to be the supervisors (indeed to such a degree that the Kenyan worker/ Asian manager has become a stereotype), it also seems possible for Kenyan workers and an Asian manager to form a team in which the Asian is more or less integrated into the teamwork while maintaining an edge.

This type of teamwork happens most frequently in small enterprises where the Kenyans can function virtually as apprentices to the Asian specialist. Although Asian masters do train Asian apprentices, who then become masters in their own right, there is no apprentice/journeyman/ master system in the learning of trades. The Asian specialist's Kenyan workers, whether they have formal training or not, never advance to the level of master. The efforts of the state to license and regulate these streams of training requires more cooperation from (or more licensing of) the artisans than is now possible.

An Asian electrical contractor can hire several Kenyan assistants to perform the mechanical work under his immediate direction, and the association may approach teamwork. In this way, however, the teamwork can actually limit the Kenyans' ability to gain managerial positions or status of independent tradesmen. Undercapitalization—the artisans' complaint of limited loans—makes it difficult to obtain the equipment and goods required to operate a contractor's trade. A Kenyan skilled enough for independent work may remain an "apprentice" to use the master's tools and stock.

Where there is Kenyan management, limited capital still dictates the form but on a larger scale may actually serve the conduct of teamwork. Barn'getuny Plaza proceeds by fits and starts as the promoter obtains additional capital for materials and labor. Bricklayers face the cement shell with courses of brick, cease operations, and return as the bricks are delivered. This piecemeal building is well suited to the independent teamwork

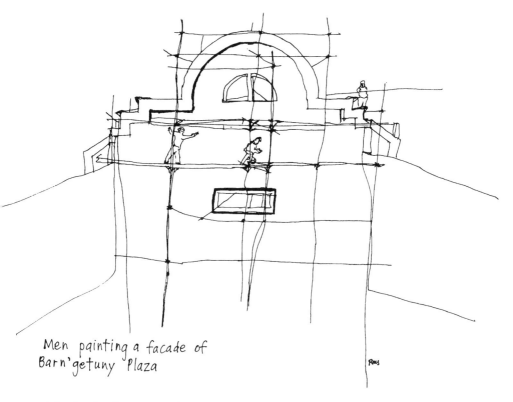

Men painting a facade of
Barn'getuny Plaza

of the fundi. They can perform their task in a unit determined by supply,
knock off, and return when the financing is available.

The same cement and plaster construction is used everywhere. After
the foundation is laid and the walls and roof are put in place by heavy
equipment, the building can grow slowly. Neither weather nor vandalism
is likely to bring it down. The very different financial structure of commercial building in Eldoret makes abandoned shells extremely unlikely.
This serves both promoter and workers since the slowly progressing
building is always a good investment and always potential work. Eldoret
already has a glut of office space, but new structures take so long to complete that the consequences will not be felt for a while.

Small villages provided with three-story community centers or bank
buildings attest to factors other than supply and demand. Barn'getuny

Plaza, like other similar structures, fits so well into the way things are made in Eldoret that it almost manages itself. Those who perform teamwork upon it are managed by the wish to continue doing so sometime in the future. Of course, the same ethnic considerations guide the social form. The management style of the Eldo Center contractor compensates for his ethnic difference and the short term of the project.

The Uasin Gishu District Hospital on Nandi Road has been undergoing expansion to become a teaching hospital for Moi University's Department of Health Sciences for several years. New student dormitories were built on one side of the road, and now the hospital building itself, a three-storied structure, is well under way. The management and engineering expertise is provided by the People's Republic of China either through government ministries or directly in the form of Chinese experts. Even the earthmoving and structural equipment was loaned by the Chinese for the early, heavy phases of construction and taken away when no longer needed.

The project has not been interrupted by undersupply but has shown continual progress by teams working on a multitude of independent and related tasks: establishing the drainage system (though this, too, is quite imperfect as evidenced by the condition of the road), dressing the stone, finishing the concrete facing, laying cement floors on upper stories, installing plumbing and electrical lines for the work and the finished project, and maintaining security.

All of this labor is provided by Kenyans of varying levels of skill. The Chinese experts, like the laborers, live beside the construction site in long corrugated aluminum buildings thrown up for that purpose. Their interaction with the laborers is complex. To some degree, the Chinese experts play the part of the ethnically different managers, an effect that is exaggerated by the presence of Kenyan managers who mediate between the laboring teams and the Chinese. Several of the Chinese speak Swahili and English, though not always in a manner understandable to managers and workers. The continuing provision of materials and equipment and the need to show progress has most strongly contributed to perpetuating this mesh of managerial and teamwork forms, which deserves a sociological study in itself. That would be necessary to look any more deeply at

the array of technologies in this project, since Kenyan ways of imple-
menting even a basic technology frequently run against Chinese biases.
Since the Kenyans supply coordinated energy, their teamwork surpasses
any revisions of management.

This and other construction settings provide the best sight of Kenyan
teamwork and management at play with outside managerial effects and
the interplay of technologies. These are overwhelmingly male enterprises. Women are confined to provisioning the workers (which they also
accomplish as a team) and performing domestic tasks as wives or female
relatives. Women can work in teams as well as men, and at the same
tasks, but child care and domestic demands have generally prevented
them from taking part in work on the same scale as men. Mixed teams
appear to be out of the question, though women work crews are always
under a male supervisor. Women's experience in farm labor and marketing is at times adapted to road labor but without the specialized tasks that
men are afforded.

Because the work assigned to women by role is everyday work, wom-
en's teamwork has an even deeper cooperative basis than men's, and the
management is less external to the task. There are in Eldoret several
shops of women cloth workers and hairdressers; some even combine these
two forms of work and include typing services. It seems that when women
form a shop, it is likely to incorporate whatever is considered legitimate
for women to do.

One combination of teamwork and management amid contrasting
technologies was constructed when an Asian-managed contracting firm
was remodeling a hair salon run by a Kenyan woman. The proprietress,
two subordinate haircutters, and two girls employed to sweep up and go
for soft drinks went about their individual business serving three customers, and two who were waiting, while the men brought in and installed the first of several sinks and used a radial saw to cut wooden frame
sections for a new doorway. The team maintaining the whole condition
was mixed, self-managed, and managed from outside.

Trash removal in Eldoret is also the work of paired teams of men and
women, teams that parallel and mimic the agrarian division of technology and labor. The women, about ten in all, pilot wheeled trash cans

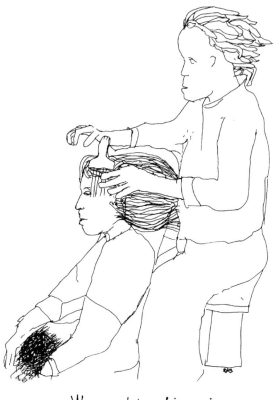

Woman doing kinyozi

down the streets, sweeping refuse into little piles that they later collect into their cans. This refuse is in turn deposited in dumpsters in the central market and on the streets. The dumpsters are emptied periodically (but according to the women, not often enough) into a new dump truck that was donated with the dumpsters by a Danish aid organization.

The dump truck is driven by men. It brings its load to the municipal dump where scavengers of both sexes can pick it over. There are, of course, teams of male scavengers who attempt to go through the refuse at any stage of its disposal. Their teamwork consists in the systematic coverage of territories, but the influx of "Nairobi style" scavengers, with their blackened clothes and glue-sniffing bottles, has threatened this entente.

Growth of and changes in the working population of Eldoret brought a response from the municipal authorities. On 6 September 1990 the Eldoret Municipal Council promulgated a notice that all "informal sector" artisans practicing in Eldoret were thereafter required to be in possession of a valid license to be permitted to practice their trade within the city. The artisans were required to come to the town clerk's office and pay a fifty shilling fee for an application form, which they were then to fill out and return to the same office. The council listed ten categories of artisans considered subject to this decree: jua kali mechanics, welders, scrap iron dealers, carpenters, electricians, tin smiths, metal fabricators, sign makers, tailors, and a catch-all category, "others."

This action was an attempt to make the informal more formal and to exercise more direct control over the proliferating artisans. The government policy of sponsored unions had not been very effective in getting the artisans to pay taxes, no less to register. The list of trade types that the council provided gives the bureaucratic view of this realm, but it is certainly not exhaustive or evenly delimiting in its categories; metal fabricators are often scrap iron dealers and auto mechanics, and so on.

But the council was not interested in making an ethnographically testable list of native categories. They wanted to fence off the artisans, separating them from the professionals and the experts who used more elaborate technology, had degrees, and were engaged in developing Eldoret. They were implying that the only allowable teamwork would be mechanical in nature, that the artisans are separate from each other unless supervised to work together on a project, and that solidaristic (organic) action by all artisans, whatever their specialties, is not to be considered. The jua kali cooperative competition among shop team members was, if at all visible to the officials, a threat to the order of the community, an order defined progressively as "cleanliness."

10. Decisions

Living in Eldoret requires technological expertise of everyone. The precision and attentiveness of a fundi is only a refined and specialized category of this expertise. To cross a street or make a purchase means participating in a milieu that demands different kinds of judgment.

The universal presence of machines and their all-occupying modes of production is one aspect of this judgment. Accommodation is required when people from areas less intensively mechanized encounter the Eldoret environment, but it is easy to oversimplify the kinds of contact that result. Many of the people coming to Eldoret from villages have had as much contact with machines as anyone in the city and indeed may have come to the city in order to find parts for machines. The "naive shamba boy meets big city mayhem" story tells little about technology and people in Eldoret. Everyone is in the same place here, but each person's experience already is different.

Some general patterns of judgment permit gain and minimize group hazard. They encompass issues of chance, risk, safety, and intention, philosophical issues that arise while crossing the street amid traffic or purchasing something from within a matrix of engineered criteria.

An Asian (Indian) merchant who owns two of the more progressive-looking stores in the downtown area was approached by a man who offered to sell him twenty five-cubic-centimeter phials of "red mercury" for 20,000 shillings. So it was labelled and so it appeared to be. The merchant paid the money expecting to be able to sell the "radioactive" mercury at a much higher price than he paid, since anything radioactive is legally (and in practice) unobtainable in Kenya. When he took the mercury to a dealer in Nairobi who handled such substances, he was disappointed however. The man took one look at the phial and according to the merchant, cracked it on his desk "like an egg." The mercury ran out leaving a red powder behind. The merchant then tried to sell the mercury to medical labs at the hospital to recoup something of his loss.

This is an old alchemists' trick that becomes a morality tale, but that is not its interest here. The merchant was taking a speculative, not a medical, risk. Even if the stuff was what he was told it was, he would not be able to see it to know that for sure. It would have to be shielded to prevent it from spreading its radiation. That the merchant did not know that there is no such thing as red mercury, radioactive or otherwise, immediately told the con man that he had a gullible mark.

The red mercury scam must have been at the beginning of its brief life then. Scarcely nine months later, a humorist writing for the lifestyle section of the Sunday *Nation* newspaper could describe his disastrous journey with a friend to Wajir (the Kenyan boondocks) in search of a lake of red mercury, which he clearly expected his readers to understand as a nonesuch.

The merchant, on the other hand, must have been accustomed to obtaining goods this way, from unknown parties without known connections. To him, the anonymity of the seller simply signaled a familiar source of inexpensive merchandise, not the work of a cheat who could not be pursued. His decision to purchase was made in ignorance of one danger (radioactivity) that should have been there but wasn't, and of another (fraud) that was there, but he didn't notice. The merchant's decision exposes a useful linear decision model: an act is precipitated by a motive that is divorced from the actual circumstances, but fits them in some technical way. The act itself is committed by two separate people, the actor and the one who sets up the circumstances of action.

The main condition of this model is the deficit of technical knowledge on the part of the actor, or his/her dependence upon an interested second party for that knowledge. The decision comes from knowing one set of conditions without recognizing a material state bearing upon the decision. It is common, for instance, for sellers in the various markets of Eldoret to tally up purchases using a ballpoint pen on the skin of the hand.

Cheap ballpoints (three shillings each, up to five with inflation) are the most common writing instruments in Eldoret, and their ability to write on almost anything makes hand tallying practical. However, the writing instrument and the symbolism of addition do not amount to numerical accuracy. Often people set down a column of figures and go through a painstaking process of marking down and carrying over sums only to arrive at the wrong total. The reason for this innumeracy is best sought in the teaching of arithmetic and the quality and extent of schooling, but in this instance, it fills the role of absent knowledge in a decision model. The incorrect tabulator convinces him/herself and the customer that the sum is correct, and the gain/loss is unbalanced. The decision is completed, and the exchange made on that basis.

A clerk at a bakery, receiving a one hundred shilling note for a forty-eight shilling purchase, asked the customers to give her two shillings for which she would return fifty shillings change. She probably was not trying to cheat the customers out of four shillings, but had mentally transposed the directions of payment. In this case, the customers refused the offer, requiring her instead to give over the fifty-two shillings change.

The introduction of electric cash registers in a few of the indoor supermarkets has not entirely circumvented the operation of this procedure. When a clerk rang up four light bulbs instead of three on the register, and the customer pointed this out, instead of subtracting the price of one from the total, she set about adding up the total for three manually, an operation she was unable to complete without outside help.

People who are able to calculate by eye the required bore of an engine cylinder or the load that a triangular truss can safely bear still may not be able to find the sum of a column of three four-digit figures in a commercial transaction because the decision is based on a mathematical skill (addition) they do not possess but is made within a framework they believe they can manage. This resembles the error structure characteristic of people using technology that is new to them (Rasmussen, Duncan, and Leplat 1987). Some of the technology is indeed new, either to the person or to the group as a whole. The pattern of deciding "as if but without" shows an immediate and improvisational adaptation to new structures. It is working technology without the underlying science or even the arithmetic. These are people drawn into a world that did not exist around them when, or if, they were in school.

This conclusion about error structure does not lead to more anecdotes of ineptitude but rather to an appreciation of the adaptation to, and of, technology that takes place when "fundamental" skills are imperfectly developed. The people of Eldoret achieve this adaptation by elaborating a basic decision model rather than exchanging it for a new one and adopting foreign knowledge and skills. This is neither the result of ignorance nor hidebound conservatism, nor cute and clever making-do with what there is. The operation of an underlying capacity to make things work as appropriate to the social and cultural circumstances of their operation forms a flawed decision model (taking only these circumstances into account) that yields both successes and errors. A full account of the technologies and peoples of Eldoret is impossible without recognizing the model and its seemingly contradictory manifestations in the everyday life of the city.

The Ghanaian philosopher Kwasi Wiredu discusses an analogous problem in the behavior of mechanics in his native land when they set gaps in automobile distributors: "A gap of this narrowness cannot be accurately set by the unaided eye; so car manufacturers have made feeler gauges for this purpose. However, without some form of persuasion, a Ghanaian mechanic will often not use a feeler gauge in adjusting the contact breaker point. . . . It is due, I believe, to their having been brought up in a culture that places no special value on exact measurement" (1980: 13). Professor Wiredu's observation, which is set in a far-ranging discussion of African modes of understanding, is seconded by the Nigerian academic J. Olubi Sodipo who, referring to the "virus" of resorting to one's own technical and intellectual resources, cites the technological accomplishments of the Ibo people, saying that "if you wish to purchase a good, even though non-living, copy of a human being you will find it in Aba market" (1992:14). The state of the economy cuts Africans off from manufactured parts supply, and they rise to the occasion, producing duplicates of the parts they need, but the consequence is a perpetually underdeveloped state of technology since the clever mechanics never learn how to make measurements or generalize their skills into a substitute industry. They make do with sufficient technology when they could carry on a national project served by science. This is not an attempt to explain Kenyan, Ghanaian, or certainly African "underdevelopment" on the basis of generalizations from a few examples. At the very least, it would be necessary to consider the institutions linking economic growth with scientific knowledge, as Rosenberg and Birdzell have done in their study of the emergence of Western technology (1990).

Sodipo (1992:32) speaks of a project of the University of Science and Technology in Kumasi, Ghana, "involving and accommodating the so-called roadside mechanics in the outreach programmes of its Faculty of Engineering and Technology," but he admits that he is unaware of what success the program achieved. In 1978, the Kenyan National Academy for the Advancement of Arts and Sciences claimed that "one challenge for Kenya's future policy on technology will be how to capitalize on these indigenous skills" (Khamala 1980:111), but little was done to explore that option because the government concerned itself instead with the political affiliations of the artisans, and the perceived threat to formal industries. What is left in Ghana, Nigeria, Kenya, and many other countries is a decision model that, in spite of the ingenuity of the operators, concentrates determinedly upon the immediate problem, at times disastrously, instead of on measurable, humane, and productive prospects. Although there is a Western belief in the simple practical man or woman whose practice is superior to (or more immediately useful than) the theories of the scientist or the procedures of the administrator, these people only seem to be remembered when they are progenitors of industries. Their ultimate successes may be others' immediate failures because of the working of decisions.

An example of the decision model at work in Eldoret is the trip that several matatus regularly make from the Agip gasoline station on Nandi Road to Kenyan Cooperative Creameries on Nairobi Road on the outskirts of town. Many people take this inexpensive trip to reach the workers' residences near the EATEC factories and the creamery, or to go into town from those heavily populated locations. Because this is an unprofitable trip for the touts and drivers, they try to maximize the number of passengers even beyond the dense packing of longer trips to other destinations.

The fundamental decision model is to balance leaving with those who are already in the cabin against waiting to accumulate still more passengers. The trip is a short one, no more than fifteen minutes, and the matatu can fit in more trips if it moves with fewer passengers. The passengers prefer to leave as quickly as possible with the smallest crowd that can be managed, and they may express that wish out loud as the pressure grows. It is most likely to be the high cost of fuel that decides the matatu operators in favor of fewer, denser trips. That is the model on which the matatu's progress is understood to operate, regardless of how the passengers express themselves.

This local matatu decision model in practice tends toward a cycle of diminishing returns because that practice means trying to pack many people into a space that can always hold a few more people. There is no set time of departure or schedule for arrivals. People are added as long as the tout can add them. It may be that the tout and driver disagree, and the driver makes his point by starting to move the matatu slowly across the drive while the tout stands holding the door. Both are aware that a number of people are waiting nearby for the vehicle to start before they actually board, and each has his own way of encouraging them to enter. When the people do crowd into the back in response to the start, the driver does not continue along the road but turns the matatu through the gas station lot and back around to the matatu stop, where more people may be waiting to board. The transport may take this course two or three times, receiving more people each time, before it actually is under way.

There are two separate applications of the same decision model in this sequence: that of the matatu crew, who want to maximize profit in the form of carriage, and that of the passengers, who want to minimize time lost and crowding. The model is the same, but the aims are different. The element that the crew ignores is fuel expenditure; starting up and running such a heavily burdened vehicle in circles may cut into their small profits. The passengers are pressed between comfort and travel and can be lured into discomfort for the sake of travel, or so the crew believe.

The flaws in this decision model do not prevent it from being the guiding assumption of the operation, which then takes on the character of the whole. The flaw often lies in an unawareness of what goes into a total, whether it be a substance, a sum, a trip, or an arrangement. Telephone wires show this as well.

On the back streets or across yards, even at times along the main roads, are many-stranded bunches of wires resembling frayed cables suspended between poles. These are telephone lines. Their outward condition is the result of another application of the same decision model. When a line fails to receive service (and neither nonpayment of a bill nor system failure is the cause), the defect must be traced through the line. Because telephone service does not have the dangers of electrical supply, a wire can be opened and tested without turning off the flow. Crews test the wires in a mass until they find the problem, and then they perform the necessary repairs. Test switching is in effect performed manually, by going from wire to wire until the responsive one is found. If none is responsive, it may be necessary to run a new wire to the trunk; hence, some lines have an almost organic growth of strands. Nevertheless, repair work is still, for the most part, efficient and effective.

The hit-or-miss construction of telephone lines is due to the existing system's limited capacity to detect and switch signals. The bunched wire condition of the visible lines shows externally their electronic condition. Just as the physical location of a signal is arbitrary in a mass of wires and has to be sought manually, so the location of a number may not be finely enough specified within the system. Callers of the same number may consistently reach the same wrong number. The signals are bunched, as the wires are, due to insufficient detection.

The confusion is attributable to a rapid increase in the number of subscribers within the Uasin Gishu system and the advent of faxes and other strains on the system. A signal entering the line "decides" its own course on the basis of inadequate information. The users attempt to employ the technology as it is intended, but they do not possess sufficient information or the capacity to generate the right kind, which is not always possible to do. The act is based upon an erroneous assumption suggested by technological form.

The telephone system is probably the greatest single source of conflict between those who proceed upon the immediate-effect decision model and those who expect a firmer grounding of acts in overarching technological, scientific, and administrative systems. A German biologist resident in Eldoret found one evening that his telephone was not working. The line was simply dead, and since a cursory examination showed him that there was no immediate damage to the equipment, he went the next day to the old post office in downtown Eldoret, where the telecommunications division of Kenya Posts and Telecommunications is headquartered. There he learned that as far as the billing department was concerned, his account was square; his service had not been cut off due to a perception of nonpayment (not an uncommon event in Helmut's experience). The flaw had to be in the workings of the line itself. At the enquiries desk outside the billing office, Helmut was given a hand-cranked unit that put him in touch with the engineering department in the complex out back. They answered promptly, heard his problem, took his number, and gave him a repair code.

Weeks passed, and Helmut's frustration was exacerbated by a growing family crisis at home in Germany. He returned to the telecommunications office repeatedly, received several different numbers, but no repair service. Various reports and rumors formed themselves into explanations: robbers, or the telephone crews themselves, were stealing the telephone cables to sell the scarce copper, or the district commissioner had usurped existing phone lines for his own purposes. There were no explanations from the telephone engineers beyond some vague words about underground cables and points of connection.

Helmut could not believe that the telephone company was not in control of service to his phone, thus he felt that the failure to restore it was deliberate. He offered a bribe to anyone coming to his residence to claim it after his phone came back. He imagined ethnic conflict within the company and incompetence of the work crews. His angst arose from the opinion that they could help him if they wanted to, but failed to do so for some social and technological reason. Finally, belatedly made aware of an important event because his phone still was not working, Helmut descended upon the engineers, calling them liars and weepingly accusing them of causing him harm. Four hours later, his phone was back in operation.

It may be that Helmut succeeded in shaming the engineers into doing their job by dropping his public face of order and reason and laying blame directly on them; it may be that he entertained them with a tantrum and they good-naturedly complied with repairs. The difference in values between Europeans and Kenyans can sometimes be transcended in obviously extreme states, and a display that would disgrace a Kenyan and make him into a laughingstock might convey a more serious message coming from a European. It is more likely, however, that Helmut's behavior alerted a supervisor to an instance of maintenance failure.

The supervisory structure of the telecommunications division of KPTC is based on the administration of job orders. Work in the field is done by crews who receive a daily roster but may not have the means to reach the sites of service. The field supervisor has considerable autonomy and not much coordinating contact with the main office and his chief. A crew had been sent to repair Helmut's phone and had reported the task accomplished, so no further investigation was undertaken.

Each time Helmut appeared at the office it was taken to be a separate problem, not a continuation of the original one, no matter what Helmut said. There were so many breaks in service due to windstorms, unseasonable downpours, and theft-sabotage that no one was tallying the number of notices from individual lines. No statistical survey of complaints or of maintenance activity existed to introduce quality control into telephone maintenance. The maintenance director, Mr. Macharia, was too occupied with the apportionment of scarce resources and the processing of compensation claims to follow general patterns within the response structure. However, when Helmut came that final time, he personally became a problem for the maintenance department, and they treated it as an emergency, like a call from the State Lodge or the district commissioner's office. They proceeded immediately to examine the connections of Helmut's line, reestablish service, and *then* verify the result with Helmut.

Whether the work crews that set down the phone as working were lying or were actually convinced by their own criteria that it was working, the gap lay in communication with Helmut himself. The crews' decision model did not correspond with Helmut's. While they could routinely convince themselves and their bosses that all was well, Helmut himself required more objective evidence. He succeeded in pressing his claim by creating an obligation to communicate with him as an individual that abrogated the spurious objectivity of the telephone manager's decision model and temporarily substituted his own.

It is an interesting capacity of this decision model that it often seems to force form to follow function. The history of technology has been overlaid by a history of design intended to convince consumers that the techniques and devices are user friendly. Radios and computers began as massive electronic instruments and became small, manageable, affordable packages. There even have been design types ("streamlining" for instance) in which a design form with a particular kind of appeal attempts to dictate a technology all its own. The design that emerges in Eldoret technology is a surface effect of decisions based on poor information. Design here is not the deliberate work of an industrial engineering department, but the overall effect of the operation of this decision model.

Welding artisans, although among the most skilled everyday technicians, are also subject to the flawed decision model. Their training includes strict instruction in safety precautions for using the energies they employ, and the tenor of safety practice among welders is in keeping with this training. However, errors seem again to conform to the pattern of decisions confidently made with inadequate information. The Eldoret *Weekly News* reported on Thursday, 5 November 1992, the "Inferno in Eldoret" that resulted when a jua kali welder applied his torch to the exhaust pipe of a matatu. Efforts to douse the fire with water only increased the flame, and all the firemen could do when they arrived was scoop up sand from the street and toss it in the direction of the fire. The matatu owner was reminded that artisans take no responsibility for the work they perform.

Artisans' training is itself a function of this same model, leading to their willingness to leap into a task without first looking since they are placing at risk someone else's property. On the same principle, welders can be seen working on truck gas tanks on the road to the creamery, and the absence of serious mishaps is no tribute to their welding ability; torches ignite gasoline vapors wherever they meet them. The matatu owner assumes that a welder will not incinerate his vehicle because the welder is trained and bears him no malice, but the welder is just a welder, not a safety inspector. The welder sees only the ruptured seam of the exhaust pipe in need of repair, and he gives no more thought to traces of gasoline than he would to the proximity of the Opera Cafe to the scene of the mishap. Such reasoning recalls Benjamin Lee Whorf's insurance case-book examples of verbal habit reigning over concrete inspection, leading to destructive fires: "We always assume that the linguistic analysis made by our group reflects reality better than it does" (1956:137).

The "inferno in Eldoret" dramatically suggests the operation of the decision model in the work of welders, whether in their taking a seam to be closed when it only looks that way, or doing good work without a shield or goggles. One can proceed for a long time making decisions on this basis with accidents happening infrequently because of improvisational wit, but the decision model will still manifest itself in the larger design.

This kind of overall design means that technological systems are likely to fail catastrophically, and those using the systems develop through experience and intuition a sense of how to prepare for this and even how to induce it for technological and other reasons. The systems used in Eldoret are not so coherent or so powerful that their failure will kill many people or produce an international media spectacle of the order of the space shuttle Challenger explosion, which apparently resulted from a similar handling of risk (Martz and Zimmer 1992).

The gravest instrument in common effect of this precarious model is the internal combustion engine, the outcomes of which (high traffic fatalities, damage to property) have already been described, but the following anecdote further illustrates the decision model's flaws.

A crowded bus climbing the slopes of the Elgeyo escarpment into the city developed a seriously overheated engine. The Nissans used in commercial bus fleets have an engine in the front of the cabin, with access beneath a cover beside the driver. As the engine grew hotter, the driver removed the covering over the radiator cap and prodded a safety valve in the cap to release overheated water. At a stop, testing it again, he drew a canvas covering over the cap and turned it, causing a geyser of hot water to erupt past him and onto the passengers seated nearby. No one was seriously burned because there was no great volume of steam, only overheated water. The driver then called for fresh water and poured pitcher after pitcher into the radiator, apparently without cracking the engine block. He had taken two chances—of injuring himself and passengers and of disabling the bus—and had succeeded for the time being in achieving his immediate end: cooling the internals of the bus in advance of the final climb. The behavior of superheated water when released under pressure with growing altitude (diminishing air pressure) was either unknown or negligible to him. The frame of reference that included personal safety and long-term concern for the equipment was not incorporated into the driver's decision model. The reasons why the bus overheated in the first place belonged to the past. When the bus later suffered a blowout and the crew could not mount the spare because they lacked the right size socket to remove the nuts, the level of failure overtook any ability to counter circumstances with force.

The decision model seems also to be systematic; that is, a number of people subscribe to it in the same way and under the same circumstances. The bus crew—driver, conductor, and assistant, as well as the maintenance people in the garage—did not anticipate the event of a flat tire on the level of actually equipping the bus to change the tire. Difficulties like this can arise within the most tightly ordered system when certain, even common, effects are unanticipated or not provided for because of low funds. I call this a decision model because it is a positive way of taking such circumstances into account by ignoring them. To the engineer or the systems inspector, this looks like wrongheadedness. The successes that follow the application of this model can come as a surprise to those with more precisely measured models; the disasters often seem predictable.

I am not developing a case for a "prescientific" dwelling on immediate cause and effect only among Kenyans. It is easily demonstrated that such a mentality is universal, and visible in its manifestations alongside "scientific" reasoning, as in the case of the nuclear plant workers who opened pipes in their facility when a pump malfunctioned, releasing quantities of contaminated water. They treated the malfunction as a plumbing problem and not as a breakdown in a more specific process of energy transfer. The governing system itself may have been defective.

Instead, I am developing a case for the endemic resort to a model to which anyone is susceptible but which is common in this region because of a combination of extrinsic factors: undersupply of materials, limited education, and low emphasis on prevention. The conditions under which failure becomes an investment in further development of design, which Petroski (1985), for instance, describes as the evolution of civil and mechanical engineering models, are conditions not often met in Eldoret technology.

It might even be appropriate to say that the common decision model is both the product and inducement of a stratum of behavior that makes a virtue of enduring what might have been forestalled with planning or conceptualizing the entire system. The human epitome of this model might be the steely pilot who forges ahead, identifying with the forward motion of the mechanism while neglecting the plane's and his own systematic frailty. We have learned to regard this person as a hero, whether he pulls through or not. The Kenyan counterpart is the matatu driver who reaches out to wipe the rain off the windshield of his vehicle when the wipers stop working during a violent storm—and ends up driving into a chasm.

Social practice provides another good example of decisions dangerously modeled. Many Kenyan communities require young men, and in a few cases young women, to go through circumcision upon reaching young adulthood. As the foreskin is cut from the penis, the initiate is to remain completely still and not show any signs of pain. Women are expected to cry out during clitoridectomy, but they can be held down. Those who go through this trial typically become ardent advocates of its application to others. They scorn members of such communities as the Luo who do not practice circumcision (though the Luo have their own trials of endurance). In the use of technology, this endurance test of group membership readily feeds a model that either knows no danger or ignores it.

Circumcision does not bring about this viewpoint; it's just one more example of the same model. People can bleed to death under the knife, die of infections, or receive a dose of disease because the same knife is used from one candidate to the next. Where female circumcision is practiced, an often explicit element of male domination is present. From the viewpoint of biomedical health practitioners, circumcision is practiced under a decision model that accepts the known risk of death or infection in the drive to affirm an all-enduring person. "Traditionalists" reject the compromise alternative of hospital circumcision because the test of adulthood and the fellow feeling of an age group circumcised together are lost. This begins to sound like the judicial and medical debate over witchcraft: even if you show me the worms in the stools of an ill person, I can always say that a witch made them develop inside him. The boy has had his foreskin removed, but that does not mean he has been circumcised. Circumcision means "facing the knife," not merely being cut by it.

Sometimes, the knife that must be faced is a machine. Besides motor vehicles, one of the most common and powerful technologies used in Eldoret is farm machinery. During the main harvest at the beginning of the dry season, usually January or February, the petrol-powered maize hullers are in use. The huller is a vertical hopper that receives the dried, husked cobs. The cobs fall onto a rapidly spinning toothed wheel that strips away the kernels, which then fall through a mesh and pour out a chute. The hopper sends the bare cobs rocketing out the front. Although other technologies, moving ramps for delivery and wheeled bins for collection, are called for by the design of the unit, they seldom are available. Instead, the maize is fed into the hopper by a man who climbs onto it and stands astride the flared metal to receive a bag of maize cobs handed up from below, which he empties into the works. The maize kernels are collected by someone, usually a woman, holding a sack to the chute while the cobs fly past, and often into, her face. Both men and women perform this routinely, with the man in the bravura position risking his legs on top while the woman stays below, with great risk to her eyesight.

The artisan who labors according to the decision model knows how the materials work and what may happen if they are placed in a certain order, but he does not concern himself with the bottom half of the equation. Whatever may be there, climatic conditions or the inflammability of volatile fluids, the unawareness of effects gives a shape to the certainty of what is known, or a certainty to the shape of what is known. So accidents are only the dramatic manifestation of the decision model. Other consequences are less dramatic and less accidental.

Soft drinks are widely consumed in Kenya and in Eldoret. Both local brands and international labels are available. Whole sides of buildings in Eldoret are blazoned with red and white Coca-Cola advertising. A bottling plant on the outskirts of the town employs more than a hundred people, many of whom live in a company housing estate named Coca-Cola. Red and white company cars and red and white buses ferry about employees. EATEC and the textile mills also paint their buses with company colors. Coca-Cola's soft drink regime is, of course, just an extension of multinational corporate imagery. The company has consistently promoted a few image components throughout its history: the red and white colors, name script, the bottle shape. Conspicuously absent is evocative figural advertising on signs or trucks or paraphernalia. One unmistakable presence, however, is the bottles. The Coca-Cola bottles are grouped together with similarly shaped bottles of Bitter Lemon and a local orange drink. It is easy to select them because of the color, but Coca-Cola is one alternative among a few in a system of soft drinks. Despite the effort to advertise it into distinctiveness, it merges into a category of "drinks," which in turn become a matter of bottles.

This already hints at the design that has emerged in the soft drink realm despite attempts to channel it more specifically to brand names. The drink is its bottle, and its bottle is its glass. Glass is another of those precious recycled materials in Kenya. Sellers of soft drinks, both the distributors and hawkers, monitor the consumption of the drink and reclaim the bottle afterward. There is no danger of a struggle over the disposal of discarded glass. The bottle with the liquid inside is carefully transported, claimed, and returned. Sale and consumption are small moments in a cycle that begins and ends at the bottling plant. Decisions keeping the bottles within the loop form a design, and there are few accidents.

Five women in a line carry four wooden cases of soda bottles, one case held between each pair. A man walks downstairs from a restaurant holding a case of glass empties in each hand at an angle that prevents any bottle from falling out. A cyclist stacks three cases on the rear of his bicycle and walks it up a steep hill. A single bottle falls off the rear of a truck and rolls down a steep grade in the center of town, carefully evaded by motorists as if it were a wandering child. Men carry bottle openers as key chain ornaments, and they are widely sold as such. The host at a gathering greets a guest offering him a drink and opens the cap with his teeth as a sign of hospitality. A child wanders among the mountains of cases in front of a depot with a look of wonder on her face. Two men, one obviously a scavenger with his sack, descend into a drainage channel to secure a bottle that has unaccountably fallen there. An askari guards a single case of carefully collected empties at a wedding celebration. An elderly man is overjoyed when his granddaughter brings him a collection of bottles she has saved from her liquor-drinking employer. His wife will use them to make home brew.

These are the inflections of bottle design. They refer to inertial balance and other properties of Eldoret technology, including the control of fluids. What unites all these and many more instances is an assumption about the easily broken valuable body of the bottle. Special strategies of transport bring the soda from plant to consumer. The basic technology of accomplishing this requires a myriad of moment-by-moment decisions that themselves form a model. The underlying "fallacy" or "misinformation" here is that the precious carbonated quality of the water is a property of the bottle and not just replaceable contents. An assumption of intrinsic value dictates the design of soda handling and calls a variety of other technologies into play in the course of making decisions about transport and handling.

Small wonder, then, that the clever Indian merchant would think that a substance is radioactive simply because it has an unusual color and is visible inside glass. The glass sanctified the contents. A parallel to this form of the decision model is in the popular treatment of chemists' glassware in the West: it must always be processing something extraordinary, and thus warrants careful handling not required by the glass itself. But whereas the handling of glass soda bottles is a positive manifestation of the decision model, the handling of welding equipment and motor vehicles is sometimes a negative manifestation of the same model.

11. Discards

An easily neglected area of Eldoret's human technology is the constant construction of the ground surface. Compared with the moving fluids discussed in chapter 12, the ground surface changes slowly, for the most part retaining the same configuration. It is a plate reflecting the city's technological character, the overground to match the rich underground of the city.

This may seem a high-flown way to write about what most people, archaeologists included, call "trash" (*takataka*), but throwing it away establishes its collectively discarded nature and makes it part of what eventually becomes a uniform dirt. To examine this level of Eldoret, I studied the contents of eight fifty-by-fifty-centimeter squares in different parts of the city.

So far this study has focused on material culture in use (archaeology in the manner of Leone 1973). This chapter concerns material culture in disuse, the closest I can come to contemporary archaeology. Unlike genuine excavational archaeology, this study has the advantage of seeing the people using the things before discarding them.

Each of these squares has an aspect, a degree of permanence, and a rate of deposit. Each therefore has an instantaneous content of objects actually discarded, which gives way to a physics and chemistry of permanence, and amounts to a rate of deposit. What is in the square, where it lands, and how long it lasts depends a great deal on the location of a square. A smooth and empty concrete surface is bordered by a trash-filled trench; deposits on a thoroughly flattened road section accumulate on a banked curb. The material underlying the squares also has an influence. Although bottle caps are a common discard, the gravel asphalt used in roadbeds does not accept them when heated by the sun, as some fluid asphalt urban roads do, creating bottle cap collages.

In an attempt to have a collection that would be typical of Eldoret, I selected squares with as much variation of site, base material, and prevalent eroding and depositional influences as possible. All of the squares are in municipal Eldoret. I will discuss them in no particular order.

One square is on the walkway just past the entrance to the district officer's compound on the main road. The base material is coarse sand, apparently formed from the disintegration of concrete slab paving that was removed, leaving an irregular surface. The main movement across the square is pedestrian and bicycle traffic, and the occasional motor vehicle that pulls off the road. About one centimeter of the objects' raised surface was preserved, and the objects showed a surprisingly high degree of persistence, one piece remaining in its configuration for three weeks before disappearing. This may be due to the kinds of objects deposited here, and their capacity to be embossed into the ground.

At one count there were seven pieces of maize cob, five paper, three wood, and three foil. The pieces of maize cob were partially disintegrated, without any kernels. Their presence may be due to the occasional presence of a maize roaster on the corner opposite, and others down the Iten Road near the entrance to the Ministry of Manpower Development office compound. Purchasers of maize would have been able to finish eating and throw away the cob by the time they reached the corner, or while waiting to cross the street. The maize cobs were the most numerous and persistent items in the square; their numbers increased, declined slightly, and then built up again, and there were always some in evidence. It may have been tempting to discard a cob there because others were there already.

The pieces of paper in the square were ragged remains of newsprint except for one piece that seemed to be part of a poster that had been torn off an adjoining pillar. The foil pieces were the inside wrapping of small pieces of hard candy sold for .30 to .50 shillings each at tables near the maize roaster and elsewhere about town. The outside cellophane wrapping does not embed easily and only collects where there is a barrier to prevent it from being carried by a breeze, either natural or automotive.

The wood was tree bark that may have come from trees inside the district officer's compound but more likely was thrown from a passing truck bringing a load of felled pines to the Raiply plywood plant on the other side of town. The bark pieces also could have fallen off an empty log truck bumping over irregularities in the pavement at the corner.

Another square is in a rugged drive between a row of shops and the post office complex. The base here is the ubiquitous cinnamon-tan clay soil (known in soil type classification as Brown Clay), which had recently been stripped of vegetation to create a walkway between the main highway and the back road where the grain depots are located. This is mostly pedestrian territory, but occasionally a truck ventures off the highway and down the path. It is a popular location for outdoor events such as three-card monte on a collection of cardboard boxes or the exhibit of a set of remarkably ugly dolls by a traveling craftsman. The drive is too exposed for longer lasting events like medicine shows or religious testifying.

The square has an array of contents easily attributed to a source: rubber and plastic parings and cuttings from the row of shoemakers facing the post office parking lot. Shoemakers use discarded tire rubber for shoe soles, and nylon sheeting for shoe bodies. Their business is mainly refitting and repair. The shapes pressed into the ground in the square are rubber and fiber-backed plastic sheeting with curved portions cut away, tossed out because they are too small for any other shoemaking purpose. The array of shapes is consistent because the same fundi, using the same materials, are discarding them there. Also visible, but far less enduring, are pieces of waxed nylon line used to stitch together the uppers of the shoe. For a time, there was also a very rare bicycle spoke bent almost beyond recognition. This square differs from the first in location and proximity to operations. There are no maize roasters or candy sellers near the post office square, and no shoemakers near the district officer's compound square.

The third square is in the roadway at the turnoff from the highway onto a side street leading to the Hindu temple complex on Moi Avenue. It is bordered by an uplifted paving square and the very high rise of the roofed cement walkway past the storefronts, hence it receives a large number of objects that would not remain long on a flatter piece of ground.

The collection in this square resembles the others. Besides several maize cobs, there are orange peels, an empty paper nut cone, bottle caps, the plastic cover of a bread loaf, the tip of a woman's shoe heel, and scraps of paper, all with writing. There are maize roasters and shoemakers nearby, and several stores where sodas can be purchased. The nut cone was formed by rolling a piece of newspaper from a corner. Street vendors often have a plastic basin filled with these cones, which they sell for .5 shilling each. The purchaser tears the top off the cone and pours the roasted ground nuts into his mouth, tossing away the paper when empty. The cones, along with maize cobs and bottle caps, are common trash in the downtown, and the bits of newspaper may also have come from these cones. The cones are usually the largest pieces of paper discarded; any newspaper on the street probably had several intermediate uses.

Paper bits can also come from cigarette butts, the paper covering of cigarette packs, store receipts, and paper product wrapping. The plastic bread bag, clearly marked "Paul's Bakery," which has its main retail store on the highway on the outskirts of town and a smaller outlet in town, is surprising because an entire loaf of bread is not street food. It may have been blown there from a dump site or trash collection vehicle. Plastic bags are notably absent from the streets of Eldoret, although they are used for packing in all of the indoor and outdoor markets. The bags also are used to carry items such as insulation and cushioning, and pieces of plastic are used to provide secure closure of leaky screw-top bottles carrying paraffin or milk. The bags are used until they disappear. If any plastic is seen intact on the streets, it is likely to be bread plastic, which is the thinnest available and not as strong as bag plastic.

This square also illustrates the proportions of material in discards. Although paper and plastic travel down pathways of use and reuse until they reach the street, paper is more common because so much more of it is produced and distributed. At the sites where scavengers bring their gleanings to be weighed, paid for, and sorted, paper always forms a mountain compared to the much smaller heaps of plastic, wood, metal, and glass. Many of the squares resemble these collection sites in the proportions of materials they exhibit simply because of the relative amounts distributed, whether there is a long journey between origin and final discard or not. Scavengers do not collect the organic trash, the maize cobs and orange peels, which they encounter among other riper items in the dumpsters they visit, because organic wastes cannot be bundled and sold to recyclers. Apart from the absence of organic waste, the collections of scavengers represent the discard pattern of Eldoret rather well.

The trash layer of a square may not be as affected by a change in its underlayer as by a change in nearby activities. While I was monitoring one square, it was paved with asphalt and became part of a road apron, yet it soon had a collection of objects similar in content and even in proportion to what was there before the paving. None of the vendors or artisans in the area had moved. The overlayer counts for more than the underlayer.

The fifth square, on a dirt road that used to be the extension of a road crossing downtown, exemplifies the effects of a change in activities and tempo. Originally it was only a soil square, dusty in dry season and muddy during the rains. There were no artisans or vendors in the area, only a greatly raised cement block of warehouses and a bus depot. Construction began on one of the many downtown malls rising in Eldoret, and rapidly a block of small shops and stores built of wood was formed parallel to the square. From only an occasional discard, the square acquired a steady content, which changed as the businesses became established.

Scavenger boy bagging
pieces of trash

RMS

Two metalworking shops, one of them devoted to fabrication of jiko and cases, the other to repairs, deposited metal pieces and fittings into the street. The slow and heavy passing traffic flattened and fixed the pieces into the ground. When a furniture-making shop opened, a few pieces of scrap wood appeared. With time, the square became completely overlaid with wood and metal pieces like an assembled abstract puzzle. Only with the arrival of a maize roaster at the corner did the complement of maize cobs or pieces join the ensemble, but they did not last as long as elsewhere because of the traffic. Dimensional discards were rendered square level, such as a Blue Band margarine can dropped from a passing lorry.

These cans, in several sizes, are widely used as measuring cups and food containers. They are seldom discarded deliberately. The can in the square had escaped the metalworkers' and scavengers' notice and was flattened in the road. It then began a transformation that included losing its colorful enamel label, corroding into a pinkish rectangle, and turning into a plate permeated by many small, ragged breaches. It might have been carried elsewhere if an accumulation of water had not liquified the underlayer of the square enough to cause the flat can to be received into the press of other metal pieces there. The water also speeded the corrosion, and the new angles of pressure from the other pieces left only the top and bottom rim bands intact, explaining for me similar pieces in other locations.

Although a jua kali establishment developed across the road from the square, it did not alter the content much because the discarded items were no different from those discarded by the other shops. This square's texture, like that of the third square, represents a surface of increasing abundance in Eldoret where there is an exposed soil underlayer. This collection of objects is like a tide that rises and covers the whole but only lingers where water might actually collect. The square's contents have been deposited there because it is irregular, and the objects are flattened to a new surface by passing traffic. The collection forms in an irregularity in the flat surface, which is subject to deliberate filling when its collective declination becomes inconvenient. Thus, the fourth square's accumulated surface was obliterated by a load of soil dumped to compact the mud that had formed from the leak. This fourth square is not unlike an early Paleolithic site at Kariandusi near Lake Elementeita, which exhibits a collection of stone hand axes and scrapers spread across a floor where they were carried by water rushing downhill from a "factory" higher up the slope.

The fifth square, on the road to the creamery and opposite a truck repair depot, is bare earth, too, and seasonally very muddy, but it also has exposed rock worn smooth by passing tractors and pickup trucks. Few discards accumulate there because the usual sources of small items are not present and because it is on a downslope. There is a greater buildup at the base of the slope in the grassy line parallel to the river. What does find its way into this square is fluid produced by truck repair, and large pieces of the repair detritus. The main object of the square was a plastic motor oil bottle that became lodged against a spur of rock and, losing its last drops, sat there only slightly flattened until it vanished.

These bottles are reused to contain oil drained from engine pans, as well as hydraulic and other used automotive fluids. The bottles also find their way into wheeled toys, and they dangle by chains from the front bumpers of vans to warn the drivers of road irregularities that might abrade a fuel line. Trucks under repair are parked along the roadside and are the source of a considerable quantity of diesel sludge and residue that gives the surface beneath them a distinct patina. The residue carried down to the square by tire motion and water flow has invested the earth there with a permanent polish.

Of all the squares I examined, this was the least altered by human activity. After the bottle disappeared, no new artifact appeared, and the only alteration was seasonal, with the rains and dust. As an experiment, I tried depositing several small squares of different kinds of paper, including foil-backed paper from a juice bottle. None of this trash persisted beyond two days. Even an oil spill that impinged on one corner could not be detected for long.

The sixth square is about five meters from the main highway in an open field. Since it is removed from the people and object flow of the main thoroughfares, one might *expect* it to be a natural history square, revealing plant growth and seasonal changes, unaffected by human influences. In the grasses covering the square is a level of life within, on, and above the soil, and the square could turn out to be an Eldoret version of studies that have monitored a meadow or a section of woodland through natural and historical time, observing the interactions of living things and, eventually, the effects of technology as the machine enters the garden. However, the square's location shouldn't prejudice its treatment.

In the preceding chapters, I have tried to demonstrate the interpenetration of countryside and city with and through technology. All of the squares reviewed so far, even the utterly devastated ones, have hosted animals and plants. An ant walking across the tar reveals that a colony is somewhere nearby in the soil beneath a crack; a tuft of dry, stubborn grass holds on to a platform of cleared ground. The sixth square simply indicates what persists, or results, when human activity is kept at a minimum by distance.

The square is covered with deeply rooted grass that is regularly cropped by grazing cows who have deposited their wastes once in the center and later on two sides of the square. The cows are pastured here to keep the grass down so that the field can be used by the local Sikh athletic club for their soccer games. The grass in the square is regularly disturbed, but only in ways that stimulate its growth. Like the oily creamery square, it has a content that maintains itself, though this is subject to seasonal cycles and the relatively mild assaults of humans and domestic animals. The grass in the square is itself uniform; no other plants compete with it. It has created a tarmac, a natural technology of surfacing appropriate to the human influences of its place, and it is as grudging of other life as the paving in the center of the highway. When a cow leaves its droppings in the square, the many ants and beetles make short work of the addition.

The seventh square is in one of the alleys that parallel the main road. The alley runs between the backs of buildings facing the main road, or the dwellings and shops that have been built behind them. The square is between a cement drainage channel and a wall. In the square are discards dependent upon the removal of accumulation from the drainage channel. Objects that have fallen or been thrown from the buildings above easily land in the channel bed or are carried there by the infrequent vehicular traffic. After the channel is excavated, the solid contents are exposed on

Man with a mattock
clearing a drainage channel

the bank, where the square is, by rain washing the soil back into the channel.

This square has a regular pattern of exposure and envelopment in which a new frame of material, itself with no positional significance, is deposited, with the larger objects fitting into the earth layer below. Unlike the square in the open roadway near the artisans' shops, this square receives its complement of objects in loads. No heavy traffic presses them after they have been dumped there; only the pressure of soil in the slight slope keeps them where they are. Anything light or soil-like in consistency runs into the channel with the rest. A spray can that had been partially crushed by wheels remained there, rusting; an intact but probably spent lightbulb rolled into the cement channel with the rain.

Since the channel is cleared with a jembe, a perpendicular shovel that is just narrower than the channel is wide, several shovelfuls fall in tandem. The deposited debris gives the square's surface a hilly undulation that is evened by the usual erosion. Scavengers apparently pay little attention to the square's accumulation of already picked-over objects.

The last square is the most clearly archaeological of the present. It is on the border of the road leading out of Eldoret toward Kisumu, just beyond the bridge over the Sosia River, in a declivity formed by water flowing down to the river. It is covered by a layer of shattered safety glass with some shreds of red plastic. The glass and plastic, heaped near the road and spreading over the rest of the square, have been pushed or swept from the roadway along with some gravel that was not there before. The pieces are evidence of a vehicle accident but are of no interest to anyone who might collect them, so they have been shoved out of the way of further traffic. Although the rain has yet to carry any of the pieces away, some have already been reduced to sand by foot traffic. Eventually the glass will be indistinguishable from the light brown sand, like other pieces of glass that have fallen into the roadside.

A similar square could be found wherever there are motor vehicles outfitted with glass. There is nothing peculiarly Eldoret, Kenyan, or African about this square or any of the others here. They all include materials that are degrading as they would anywhere else. But these are the flooring of Eldoret just the same, and the conditions of deposit are unique to the place. If I had observed the accident that yielded this glass, I would be able to say what the connections are, but the material deposits are all that remain of that single, sudden event of intentions and actions. The distance between these deposits and the cultural specifics of the action is the same as between technology and culture. The squares permit an archaeology of this present with the advantage of letting some of the action, if not its particular virtue, be seen.

12. Fluids

There are four different kinds of running water in Eldoret: the Sosia River and the streams that enter it; seasonal drainage that also trends toward the river; water from the Elligirini-Endoroto River dam near Kaptagat Forest, processed through the treatment works in Kapsoya and piped into the town; and domestic/industrial/public sewage, which is piped into a treatment plant before being released downriver. Because Eldoret does not face the gradual or flash flooding of other Kenyan towns, it has no waterworks technology for dealing with such an event. Fluids move across and beneath the surface of Eldoret demanding a technology as deliberate as the surfacing that smooths the flow of traffic, pedestrians, and goods. The various flows must be distinguished from each other, but they aren't always distinguished so well.

Eldoret's underground is laced with supply and sewage pipes, a lattice less intricate than those beneath much larger cities (Williams 1990) but of considerable interest because it conflicts with surface flow routes. Most of the open water channels in Eldoret are crossed by water pipes. In several places, pipes cross active roadways at the surface and are periodically ruptured by the traffic, which accounts for water streaming through the dust during the driest times. (Although the water department attempts to seal the pipes, they can't bury them deep enough without changing the entire system.) The only uncompromised flow is the river, which both receives and supplies fluids. Otherwise, there seems to be a conflict between the different types of fluid transport technology.

For example, fluid waste from the rows of buildings that back on the alleys is supposed to drain into pipe trees that pour the combined stream into an open cement channel, which leads to an underground pipe connected to the sewage plant. This combination of channels, although integral in design, is less than perfect in practice. The pipe junctions at the tree are often ruptured and pour the waste against the house wall, allowing it to leach into the foundation. The cement channel fills with refuse, disrupting the flow. Where the channel has been covered with soil during construction, the fluid is shunted to the channel on the opposite side of the street through a furrow in the road bed. The new channel impedes the flow of traffic in order to pass the waste into the main drainage system. And any downpour of rainwater fills these channels and pipes beyond capacity, clogging them with trash and soil and carrying the sewage over the ground toward, but not into, the river. (The various streams of fluid are not well distinguished from each other under normal circumstances, and their distinctions vanish entirely during rainy season flow.)

During the period I have been watching Eldoret, the most noticeable alteration in the design of the town itself, more than the building construction, has been the hydrological reshaping of the main highway and its vicinity. Though the technology of the reshaping looked first to control the fluids in that one region, it was the beginning of a larger act of control that would employ technological means to effect a change in the social and ethnic design of the downtown.

Next to the post office, a row of shops selling clothes, hardware, and stationery was clearly designed with hydraulic contours in mind. The buildings form a solid block penetrated by two alleys leading to the residential side in back. A cement pavement extends the length of the block before the store entrances. It is raised a full meter over the pavement of the Agip gas station entrance at one end and slopes to meet the rising contour beside the post office drive. This slight lateral slope is contoured against a more decided downslope from the building front to the highway below. At one time, the cement pavement formed a loading dock for the hardware shops, still evident in the curbs extending from some of the shops.

Recently, the municipality extended a cement drainage canal parallel to the building frontage, cutting off access from the main road. The graded cement channel, one and a half meters broad and one meter deep,

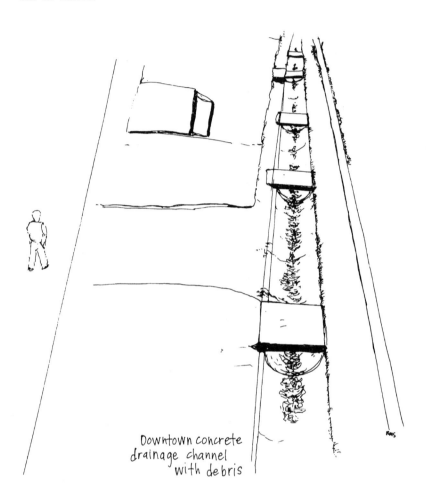

Downtown concrete
drainage channel
with debris

carries water with the trend of the road slope until it is just a rivulet at the lowest point. This lower drainage channel trends downward opposite to the slope of the pavement; thus the pavement and the drainage channel form an open "V" where they meet. The purpose of the roadside channel is to catch the water that is shed by the buildings before it floods the main road and enters the shops, not all of which are raised, or before it pours down the paved streets perpendicular to the main road.

The large channel is bridged in several places in front of the shops by paving slabs that allow pedestrians to ascend from the road. Only a hard earth apron separates the road fringe from the cement walkway, though most of the shops had covered this over with cement by the time the new channel was complete. Despite some irregularities, the ensemble of this construction is made to send falling water, according to the buildings' design, downward and forward, and according to the municipality, sideways and downward. There are two separate and more or less complementary sets of interests at work in the plan, fashioning the flow of free-running rainwater while the sewage takes its concealed route.

The Asian merchants simply want to rid themselves of the water, whereas the municipality wants to direct it. The success of either or both depends on the volume and velocity of flow. The municipality has the more difficult task because it is obliged to receive the total and send it on its way. For greater volumes of water, they do not have gravity on their side as the merchants do. Therefore, their channel is wide and deep and situated in the crease of the road to take advantage of the road's strongest trend. Across the road, in front of a row of shops, is a small cement channel backed by a concrete bar about ten centimeters high to protect the shop entrances from road flow. This channel in turn delivers to a conical storm drain piped parallel to that side of the road and into the same stream. The municipality has gradually developed along the down side of the main road a set of cement channels fringing the business area and carrying water into drainage sumps where there is a slight rise in the line that might cause the water to pool. On the down side, the channels remain underground all the way to the feeder stream; on the up side of the highway, the open channel enters subsurface pipe, which opens into another surface channel.

The overall effect of this project is to carry runoff and falling water with the steeper trend of the slope in aboveground and then underground channels to a stream, which then runs perpendicularly into the river. The hydrological engineering takes advantage of a dip that is steeper parallel to the highway than down through the town to keep the flow of water from passing through the town cluster on its way to the lowest point, the river. The contours form a cone with one side, that of the channel and pipe course, much steeper than the continuation of the road, which becomes almost flat after the post office.

Control of flowing water has been political in nature from the time of
the "hydraulic empires" of the ancient world to the dam politics of contemporary China, the southwestern United States, and northern Africa.
These attempts at control have arisen from the need to apportion water
as a resource for irrigation and for growing cities. Irrigation and urban
water issues certainly exist in Kenya, and in Eldoret in particular, but the
more immediate control issue is not one of channeling water to meet a
need but instead is one of channeling water away from where it may
cause harm. The main goal is simply getting rid of the water or, rather,
avoiding the destructive force imparted to it by its motion and by what
it carries.

The municipal water supply system has been in place for a long time,
but the water control design has lately become more conspicuous. The
hydrological contours of downtown Eldoret are a result of a shaping war
between running water and human engineering. Human engineering
anticipates a pattern of water flow predicated upon existing contours, but
then it alters the contours, which changes the water flow and requires
further response. If there were a single consistent runoff-catchment design, then all private and public engineering could be subordinated to it.
However, merchants in one area or another either have taken it into their
own hands to cope with rainy season flows or they simply ignore the
matter. Their areas of investment then interact with others constructed
differently, allowing the water to act as unpredictably as it would without engineering. The water flow that economic and social blocs anticipate
in their engineering is not the water that actually flows through the
streets.

The spate of road improvement and sidewalk construction that lately
has improved the pedestrian and automotive experience of the downtown has also necessitated protecting the construction from the ravages
of the rains. This, in turn, has required a more explicit municipal consciousness of the city's hydrology.

The name "Eldoret" was originally a Maasai phrase "ol-dore" (beside
the stony river), which is taken to refer to the stony and occasionally dry
Sosia River bed. The name gained its current form due to a misspelling on a map, a misspelling that might have served a wish to exclude Maa-

sai claims. With its "-et" suffix, "Eldoret" sounds like a Kalenjin noun (Mbwagwa 1980:14). The river was the main physical feature of the town from the start when in 1910, it was simply plot number 64 on a survey chart (sixty-four kilometers away from the railhead at Timboroa) and a post office to serve local white farmers.

The Sosia River at the base of the valley hardly qualifies as more than a stream at any point of its passage through the city. Its claim to river status may lie in the force it acquires when thousands of spontaneous tributaries carve the earth to reach the river at the lowest point in the valley. They may follow prepared channels, like those in the city center, or they may make their own way in a manner that varies with the volume of water and what it carries. Usually the water carries topsoil, which is deposited as the velocity of flow decreases at obstacles or with a change of slope. Enough silt reaches the river to impart to it a pale tea color during the rainy season. At other times, the river and its persistent tributaries vary in color from a flat white to lavender or cherry, depending on the chemical content. A chemical analysis of the water in the Nairobi River, a much larger flow, showed considerable heavy metal and organic contaminant pollution (*Weekly Mail,* 13 July 1993); the Sosia River receives many of the same contaminants (e.g., agricultural chemicals, abattoir [slaughterhouse] wastes, and dyestuffs).

Because the river is downhill from everything, it receives whatever is put into water, and the torrents of the rainy season carry whatever they come across. Throughout the year, regularly flowing streams carry human, household, and industrial waste along their courses. The main factories release the colorful products of their dyeing and cleansing operations into the channels. On a still undeveloped plot of land just above the river, trickles of foul-smelling sewage from buildings in town run across a bare terrain where men bathe in small pools of rainwater.

There is a town sewage system, and a treatment plant for processing effluent discharged into the Sosia River, but they receive only a small amount of the total waste stream. Although many facilities have septic tanks, the tanks can be sited to allow their contents to be carried by groundwater. Water is controlled for its direction and force, not for its content. The "natural" courses are not natural in what they pass along.

Local hydrology is not content but form, and topsoil erosion is of as little interest as water contamination. Water is controlled to capture it for use and get rid of it once used, carrying whatever can enter its medium. People crossing a bridge over the river in a residential area of town may release bags of garbage as they pass. A little boy entertained himself at a small dump of engine oil filters by removing them one by one and tossing them into the river. A dead cow floated for a while in the eddy on one side of the bridge. On the other side, a Christian group strung lines of flowers over a broadening of the river and held baptismal rites.

The main goals of water control are to ensure that it carries away what should be carried away and leaves what should be left. The rubbish should be removed; the roadways and sidewalks should be left. The control of water, then, is really a waste disposal operation. The path of water away from habitations and places of business must be ensured because of what it also carries. In the city, the channels are deep and have many bridges over them to restrict the contact of humans and animals with the waste stream.

East of the city, two continuous streams cross a barren area along the main road, just before two of the factories. The streams are captured in cement channels and directed through culverts underneath the highway. On the other side, one of the streams is brought around the front of the factory and sent into an earthen channel along a dirt road through a residential district. It goes beneath another paved road, through a smaller culvert than the first, and from there along another earth channel to the river. The charge of the water along the channel is at times so great that it exceeds the carrying capacity of the culvert and threatens to dissolve the roadbed and flood the adjoining area.

When the channel was dug again manually, and a stone-lined concrete basin built where the water enters, a pair of pre-formed concrete bars was laid across the channel to break the force of the current and form a spray. The bars did dissipate the water, but they also increased erosion of the earth shoulder as the water spread over the road and poured off the edge of the asphalt. The channel requires repeated manual removal of soil and vegetable matter as well as reinforcement of its precipitous earth banks.

During periods of heavy rainfall, the entire watercourse tends to revert to the condition of a natural stream as it carries effluent away from the factories. It is only the drainage policy of the municipality and the labor invested that maintains the artificially deep and narrow flow. That flow can easily turn aside when the volume exceeds the channel capacity or when the effects of an improvement in the flow structure, the cement bars for instance, are not anticipated further downstream.

The municipality also tries to control the greatly fluctuating flow of the other stream that originates in the same area. The stream passes beneath the main road through a pair of culverts and crosses a tip of land where the other paved road converges with the main road. Nandi Road, recently paved by a German firm, is the one that the lower stream was prevented from undermining. Nandi Road once entered the lower edge of the downtown, where the central market was, but now the market has moved, and the long-term construction of a hospital has all but closed the lower reaches of the road. The juncture of Nandi Road with Uganda Road has been thoroughly reconstructed, with curved tracks entering from left and right, separated by a center island sporting a sign describing the construction of the hospital.

The peninsula that tapers into the juncture of the two roads is undeveloped land separated by a fence from a field and an elite housing project. The water enters the area at two angles of descent, from the slope of its origin and along the side slope of the main road. The road construction has had the effect of exaggerating the basin-like contours of the place where the two roads meet. While the flow through the culvert remains moderate, the water passes across the peninsula, through another culvert under Nandi Road, and into a streambed that disappears beneath a fence on its way to a small pond on private property. With heavy rainfall, the water pours through the channels, which are lined only beyond the culverts, and pools over the sides of the channel cut across the land strip. Water flows in sheets down the road surfaces in three directions to gather at its hydrological destination.

The flow is given emphasis by the tubular dynamics of the pipes, and as it picks up the added mass of the sheets, the water forms a powerful turning and licking wave where the road curves backward. This has removed the soil where it is loosest, leaving the underlayer of the road deeply scooped almost to the extent of exposing the gravel base of the asphalt. The water continues the shaping work from its own side as the flow permitted by soft boundaries suddenly encounters harder material at its lowest point.

In the channel itself, the water pools more sluggishly, and because the road is raised over the land slope, the watercourse merely floods its own banks and the catchment on the other side of the road, where it forms a temporary pond. The water then glides through a narrow slatted fence, leaving clumps of dried grass and other material and forcing the fence to sag backward. That flow does not cross the road itself, but instead the road boundaries serve as a dam on both sides, making two separate ponds, one draining into the other through the culvert below. The stream's further connections cannot absorb the enhanced flow, and so it must remain in its basin, divided by the road and turning against its softer portions.

The civil engineering response to this seasonal disarray of waterworks has been to deepen and fortify the channels. After heavy rain causes a channel to overflow, workmen descend into the pit on either side of the road and with jembe (shovels) and pails remove the accumulated matter. They dig the base ever deeper to admit the amount of water coming to rest there, in effect affirming the unintended basin role of the dividing land in order to protect the road from crosscurrents. The thoroughly carved sweep of the road has received quantities of loose asphalt, which the workers pack into a solid lip against the design of the torrent. Here there is no shedding of water at cross purposes due to conflicting property interests, as in the downtown. The multiple hydrological consequences of road building are met with a defensive drainage strategy, and the edge of the water is kept away from the most valuable construction. Creating a more substantial drainage channel through private property is not considered. The municipality simply keeps the water away from its investment and passes it along.

Niemcynowicz (1992:138) describes this concept of water control as "traditional storm drainage" and "end of pipe" strategies as opposed to the "source control" he advocates. According to Niemcynowicz, traditional storm drainage is actually more "expensive" than finding ways to use the water and what it brings because it consists merely of erecting costly barriers rather than capturing the water with basic technologies. In a global context, this is an important observation. The local world of Eldoret, however, demonstrates why local control of fluids is difficult to bring into that larger context.

A scientific assessment of drainage patterns in the downtown area would immediately point to the disruptiveness of much of the construction now going on (Zuidema 1987). New building, like that already in place, is not designed with an eye to existing or likely flow patterns on or below the surface. The seventeen-story Kerio Valley Development Authority building, Eldoret's first structure over three stories in height, was erected in its present location between the Sirikwa Hotel and Uganda Road without a study of its effect upon the site and the vicinity. Of the numerous views expressed about the building, few concern the associated hydrology. It is a monument to Kenya's development and Eldoret's growth; it is a gift to his constituents from Kerio Valley South MP Nicholas Biwott; it is an office and commercial center with few of the shops and offices tenanted; and it has ruined the sight lines from the Sirikwa Hotel and given the lie to "Elgon View Terrace," since it blocks the view of the mountain. However, it also is an obstacle to the drainage being promoted by the channels along the main road.

Of course, it can be argued that ease of drainage is not the chief design function in new building, which is done in response to perceived needs and investment opportunities, not urban drainage problems. But the structural engineering of the building does not even directly address its own drainage needs. The tower form is symbolic and not concretely functional. Water channels are created to solve existing problems without consideration for an overall plan that includes control of fluids. The water that a building this size is likely to displace from its roof and sides is not given a course, and what course it had is now lost. The apparent control of water in the downtown area is as symbolic as the building that occasions it. The erosive flow runs wild in the streets, depositing its burdens where it may, before reaching the established channels.

Barn'getuny Plaza, a privately funded structure long in the making, borders Uganda Road and the main tributary channel to the river, into which both new and old courses feed. The plaza is a massive cement hulk that covers a thirty-by-thirty-meter plot. It blocks flow into the channel from two directions. The result is an accumulation of water in large pools on the dirt road in front, and the creation of a seasonally very muddy track where an access has been cut for construction equipment and deliveries in back. Mud is even less susceptible to control than the water, and throughout the rainy season, the plaza is surrounded by pools and mire. Such conditions result in a paradox: the roadways, although retaining their shape, are almost impassable for both pedestrians and vehicles.

During the dry season, the roadways dry out, and the wind and passing traffic displace large quantities of dust into the air and into the open buildings, adding maintenance costs. Construction progresses very slowly as the investors delay obtaining loans or cash to finance the next phase. Because the projects are larger and move slowly, the drainage plan of the downtown is disrupted from different sides, making uniformity impossible even if that were municipal intent. The building will look good when it is completed, but it will be an air palace, hollow and floating, as the earth around it liquifies no matter how well it is paved. The even more massive Reinsurance Building under construction across the road faces similar problems.

With the construction of sidewalks and a new channel parallel and up-slope of the main road, a general drainage plan does seem to be emerging in Eldoret, or perhaps more accurately, the conflict between the municipal desire to control water flows and the spate of speculative building is changing. Eldoret is being defined technically in this emerging conflict.

Although there is an urban plan, it is largely irrelevant to the matters of flow and control in the city, which have to do with the configuration of landforms and the nature of the flow, whether of water or traffic, and the political economy of land use and construction. It would seem to be the purpose of a government to control publicly what private entrepreneurs can ignore unless it profits them to notice them. So the control of fluids in Eldoret as a whole is part of the municipal authority's developing technological self-definition.

Water is only the most obvious example of a flow that the authority tries to control on an urban scale. Another example is traffic. Traffic, of course, flows more regularly and because of its economics, is accommodated more enthusiastically. Where water is passed through the city to the river, traffic is received into the city. Eldoret was initially defined by its role as a railway terminus, and the highly controlled progress of the trains still shapes the town. The authorities' (but not the municipal authorities') control of the trains has set them off in their own corridor apart from the main activity of the town, which is centered upon motorways. The trains, however regular their travel, are difficult to reach and uncertain of access. Their schedule is decided by commercial considerations, and their cost is extremely high compared with other transportation. Making the trip to Nairobi an overnight obscures the amount of time it takes to complete the trip (twelve hours, compared to five by bus) and adds the expense of a sleeper to the already high fare, and the need to apply well in advance for reservations that may not be available. These difficulties have shifted much of the transport of passengers and goods to the roadway, just as the rushing water, when one conduit is small or blocked, finds another channel.

Although allowing traffic to move through town is an advantage, controlling it is a problem. Providing a regularly upgraded road does not offer any greater measure of control than is accomplished with cement watercourses. Water may overflow its channels and carry undesirable elements, and so can traffic. The technology of bringing traffic to the town all too easily seems to be the means of regulating it.

As the volume of traffic through the town has increased, the authorities have begun to identify themselves as controllers of the flow by trying to separate and identify the elements they control. Thus vehicular traffic is given the roadway, and police checks give it form; pedestrian traffic is channeled by the construction of sidewalks and the marking of crosswalks; and water is confined to a growing number of trenches that parallel the road and walkways. Where arbitrary flows once moved through Eldoret, they now have names and places to go. And they are subject to different official departments whose actions ensure their separation.

Eldoret's growth as a municipal entity has been accompanied by an increasing assertion of symbolic control by defining channels of flow. This has meant construction work to keep the main fluids that have been chosen for control apart from each other and united in themselves. The

Men erecting a traffic light

strongest example of this technological self-identification is the treatment of the presidential motorcades that periodically make their way
down the main road.

Along the entire route of presidential travel, Kenyan flags are planted,
irregularities are removed, and speed bumps flattened (a special type of
speed bump has been devised for this purpose). Pennants are strung
across the road, and people line the street awaiting the passing of the
three black Mercedes and their entourage. Armed police and military
personnel are stationed at main intersections, and they route all other vehicles away from the main road to make way for the presidential traffic.
The controlling element is the flow of the motorcade.

Presidential motorcades are an unusual flux in the normal flow of goods and passengers along the route. That flow is intended to increase in two senses, in number of vehicles and in size of individual vehicles. A bonded customs warehouse and storage facility near the fuel depot and some former railroad sideline warehouses have been upgraded to a containerized shipment facility. This is related to the transformation of goods retailing and artisanship in downtown Eldoret, which will be considered later. A cross-Kenya fuel oil pipeline has also been extended from Nakuru to Eldoret, making it possible to fuel container trucks. Thus, the elements of traffic flow have become more massive.

The lack of traffic lights and regular police traffic management makes the highway flow parallel and perpendicular to the downhill water that it resembles. Traffic lights were installed on very high poles at the junction of Nairobi and Kisumu roads in the center of Eldoret, but they still had not been activated by mid-1994. The potential for control is always present, but any control is intrinsically dependent upon the physics of its flow. Just as with water, all that the municipal authorities have mandated is the channel.

13. Sign Making

Several languages are spoken in Eldoret, and each is equally able to express required technical meanings. I do not mean to sound facetious nor to imply that those meanings are so modest that any of the languages can express them, or that all the speakers use English when they speak in technical terms. There is a great deal of what linguists call code switching among speakers of the languages (writing is another matter). A speaker will begin a sentence in Swahili, then use an English phrase, and conclude with a Kalenjin expression, or even combine them in the same word. For example, *Tunngeebego* means "Let's go" and is a combination of the Swahili first-person plural plus Kalenjin "go" plus English "go."

The manner of language use may dictate a pattern of code switching with certain phrases employed only in English or Kalenjin or Luhya, for instance. Occupational groups may favor one pattern or another, often importing words and phrases from their training into the common speech. Kalenjin vernacular speakers may be able to communicate with Luhya vernacular speakers because they all have been schooled in English and Swahili and because they are united by a common practice, such as auto mechanics. This chapter, written entirely in scholastic English, is an attempt to describe this realm of discourse.

Mbaabu (1985:44–45) discusses alternating between Swahili technical terms and English ones, for instance, *kipazasauti* and "loudspeaker." The former was invented by language planners wanting to have a Swahili term for this important device. But as Mbaabu points out, usage, not language planners, decides what the word is. In fact, even in Swahili sentences, I do not hear "kipazasauti" or "loudspeaker," but *laudispika,* which may be what usage is determining.

The colloquial conversation of telephone crews is replete with language codes that reveal the impact of usage. The crew members must communicate with each other about the state of electronic connections for which there is a well-developed international vocabulary in English. In the presence of a native English speaker or a non-Kalenjin-speaking supervisor, they discuss matters in English. Among themselves, they speak Kalenjin and get technical meanings across because there is a recognized code among them. The Swahili word for "telephone" is *simu,* which basically means "wire" and has been taken over into Kalenjin as *simooit.* But workers need to speak of wires as well as of telephones, hence the word *wayaiyiaat* from the English "wire." Discussion of a switching problem in Kalenjin can be as productive as in Swahili or European languages. This creation of language that does not extend outside of the specialized situation can also serve the ethnic solidarity of the work group, who can speak of technical matters in their own language. (However, work crews for any of the technical services requiring field service are not all that uniform ethnically, and the complex shifting interlanguage of these crews cannot be easily characterized.)

New technologies usually arrive with English words attached, and those words are often retained in the language of the users of the technology. Swahili terms are constantly being devised but often are not much in circulation on the simple principle that the English word will do and seems to label the essence of the device, which will then have to be translated into other languages. The attempts of French language authorities to promulgate French terms for such pervasive English words as "computer" and "cassette" (which came from French) has had limited success in usage. Although Swahili is spreading and may become a candidate for status as *the* African language, its speakers will still be constrained to accept the English word along with the invention. They may not accept either word or technology wholeheartedly. Swahili absorbed a large vocabulary of words from Arabic, including many Muslim religious terms, the words for "sound" (*sauti*), "light" (*nur*), and "color" (*rangi*) among others, but it did not become Arabic in the process. The influx of English technical terms into Swahili and other African languages might be viewed in the same manner: the words are received without the assumptions that English speakers may not even notice.

It is an interesting question of language philosophy to consider the "fitness" of a given language to convey technical concepts adequately enough to serve as an educational medium. This touches upon the cognitive and intellectual "adequacy" of natural languages (those not deliberately invented) on the one hand and the capacity of natural languages to carry each other's semantic load on the other. To what degree is the question disinterestedly philosophical, and to what degree ethnocentric? Some contemporary Muslim philosophers have argued that the underpinnings of science and technology are themselves "Western" and can make no claim to universality.

The "fitness" of a language depends on the translatability of scientific concepts and technological constructions into that language, and the importance of maintaining that particular conceptual content while employing the devices or even conducting the research. So it is not merely a question of, "Can you explain the operation of magnetic resonance imaging in Swahili?" Instead, the questions is, "Can you explain the operation of the device in a manner suited to the speakers of the language?" How much will you insist on making the Swahili correspond to the English under the assumption that only the English wording, which includes metaphors commonly employed in English, is correct? How many concessions will you make to Swahili? If you don't make concessions, how well do you speak Swahili after all?

This is an issue basic to the poetics of technology in Eldoret. It cannot be assumed that people just get along with English when they need to refer to technology. Microwaves and DNA codons, though most often described verbally in English, do not exist exclusively in English, Swahili, or any other language. To think of them as epiphenomena of language challenges the assumption of their universality. This is not the place to enter upon the epistemology of DNA, or even to ask if there is an epistemology expressible in Kalenjin that can correspond to it. The anthropological task of making known the cosmology and ethics of "other" civilizations assumes translating those cosmologies into one of very few European languages. For example, are these languages able to convey the idea of spirituality inherent in Swahili, where one word for "spirit" (*upepo*) is the plural of "wind" (*pepo*)? Can classical Greek *psyche*, "breath," be a parallel?

Signs in Eldoret offer one answer to this question. These are public display signs, not the signs of semiotics. There are many signs about the town, the majority of them in English, although Devnagari lettering appears on some signs near the Hindu temples on Moi Avenue. Many of the signs are in color. The red and white of Coca-Cola is so prominent that other soft drinks are advertised in the same color format. All signs are verbal and of a fairly uniform style of lettering. The figural signs are advertising displays of goods and services and a large number of *kinyozi* signs showing the glamorous results of a hair treatment in the salon. These are hand-painted signs of human heads, a figure otherwise seen only in samples in the windows of photographic supply stores, on political posters, and in small-scale advertising.

The massive presence of the Roman alphabet in signs on the streets of Eldoret suggests a communication apart from what the signs say. Whatever the contest between major and vernacular languages in speech and in the schools, the public signs are in English. The signs seem to be sustaining the widespread role of English as "the other tongue" (Kachru 1982) used as a technological auxiliary and as a link to international cultural forms, especially youth and entertainment culture.

The technologies of display and reproduction—photography and photo-offset, silkscreening and xeroxing—all are used in sign making. The political campaigns that preceded the first multiparty elections in Kenya's history, held on 29 December 1992, became showcases for candidates seeking to master attention and get the support that could transcend the limitations of particular languages while keeping the support of particular language-ethnic groups. Reuben Cheshire, an incumbent running for parliament from an Eldoret constituency, had the usual posters printed with his photograph, but he also issued T-shirts with his photo likeness to supporters who wore them as they drove about in trucks with loudspeakers blaring his speeches in Swahili.

There are different species of sign makers in Eldoret, using different technologies in accord with a sign's intended use. The visual field of many cities is dominated by a uniform sign quality imposed by color offset reproduction, which makes the occasional carved or hand-lettered sign look improvised and rustic. In Eldoret, there is a clear division between painted signs, which may be monumental, and photographic signs, which are always small-scale. Signs can also be divided by form: the large signs always employ Roman letters, and the small ones employ letters and human figures. Corporate logos and trademark signs are confined to the service stations. Signs custom-made by Sportsman cigarettes appear only in shops and towns and along the roads. Increasingly common are small paper posters pasted to fences and walls advertising detergents, antimalarials, and religious crusades, and they have rapidly made inroads on the hand-painted signs.

The approach to Eldoret is now a line of baked-enamel company signs until you reach the new Shell station at the Kaptagat Road turnoff from Nairobi Road. It is aglow with the colors of its corporate signs, which have been planted up and down the main road.

The hand-painted signs are the work of sign-making artisans who obtain their training in polytechnics or as assistants to established sign painters. They paint the sides of buildings, and boards that are to be placed on buildings or left standing on road corners. The large building signs, most often soft drink advertising, display curvilinear or script-like lettering, framed and given geometric flourishes, all in the same primary color. The smaller signs invariably have squat, black sans-serif letterforms sized to distinguish capitals, on a white, blue, or yellow background. Figures and illustrations are rare. The style of sign making is so consistent within the Eldoret area that it is indistinguishable from its own technology: where paint is applied to board in letters it always looks like a sign.

Building signs for soft drinks, cleanser, medicine, and toothpaste, and most of the posters, are subsidized by national enterprises that distribute their products locally. The local stores' signs are much more modest, confining themselves to names lettered on hanging panels or a cornice. There is no display window lettering. Product promotions are signaled

Man painting a battery sign on a building wall

by marker-drawn pieces of cardboard propped up inside and by chalk no-
tations on a folding blackboard placed outside. The only mass-produced
advertising signs are film posters and stand-up figural signs in photo
stores (the significance of which will emerge later).

The main users of lettered signs are government agencies, which indi-
cate their proximity with a plain name sign on the roadside nearest their
location, frequently with the local post office box number and possibly a
telephone number. A location might be indicated, but usually there is
just the sign to mark the presence of a given ministry and an office
thereof in Eldoret. These naming boards, clustered together and planted
about the town, give Eldoret a distinctive look. Sign makers are kept busy
renewing them and adding to them. Wherever a foreign-funded public
project is under way—such as the Chinese hospital buildings or the

German waterworks—a ladder-like, tall sign is erected with individual slats naming the ministries responsible for each aspect of the work.

Mulabi is a sign maker who does plain lettering, but his forte is making signs with human faces for beauty salons and kinyozi parlors. These services spring up wherever other small businesses attract customers, because they are not a licensed trade and can be practiced by any woman or man with a pair of scissors and a manner engaging enough to keep customers returning. Because this is probably the commonest small business in Eldoret (I counted twenty-five of them in the downtown alone), those who intend to make a living by its practice need to keep their name

Aunt Super Salon
kinyozi for women, displaying
a sign

and place clearly labeled. The kinyozi do not engage in the cooperative competition that exists among the shoeshiners and fixed hawkers, which allows them to operate in rows of identical units. Mulabi serves the kinyozi need for distinctiveness with signs that are more than lettered.

Mulabi is a Kikuyu from Central Province, and he makes signs for other Kikuyu who know kinyozi by figural signs. This is a facet of Kikuyu life that has been transplanted to Eldoret. Numerous kinyozi signs appear in two alleys in particular, and in these places, the strictly lettered look of Eldoret abates somewhat. The Kikuyu cities in Central Province not only sport kinyozi and other figural signs, but entire buildings there are painted over with colored shapes of animals, plants, and people in scenes referring to the businesses housed inside.

When he receives a commission, Mulabi needs to know the name of the salon, whether it serves men or women (usually not both), and what type of hairdo the images should be wearing. As new cuts come into vogue, he will be asked to change a sign he made before or to make a new one to suggest that the parlor is up to date and vital. The one establishment in town exclusively devoted to men's cuts hired Mulabi to paint the figures of Michael Jackson and Eddie Murphy for its wooden security doors.

The head he draws on the primed hardwood plank is in profile or three-quarters view, never frontal, and is strictly a head view, without shoulders or neck. He outlines the features and the hair shape in chalk. The eyes and lips are very large, and the nose disproportionately small: these are conventions accepted by figural sign makers in other areas who draw the same way and recognize that such features are not representative of an individual but of a "beautiful" face. He paints the surface of the face in light brown or auburn matte house paint, without any modeling or contours or shadowing. He stripes in the hair with as much detail of strands as clarifying the style requires, the one aspect of his drawing that is not fully conventionalized. The eyes are set out with black irises, and the lips reddened. Women receive additional color to eyes and lips to suggest the effects of makeup. The name of the kinyozi, possibly with a list of the cuts available, finishes the work.

Where several signs appear in a row, they are distinguished by differences of execution and coloring. They are as eye-catching as the customer will be after a session at this kinyozi. Mulabi receives one hundred and fifty to two hundred shillings for a sign. (A basic haircut costs twenty to thirty shillings.)

The other type of sign made and exhibited in the downtown is exclusively a representation of the human figure: photographs. The role they play in the signscape in many other cities is sharply curtailed by the expense of even modest cameras and by the unavailability of large-format photographic reproduction. The most visible use of photography in signs is in the campaign posters already mentioned, but these grainy black-and-white offset prints are no larger than the standard twenty-by-thirty-centimeter portrait photograph. There are none of the enormous photographic posters of public personalities (politicians, singers, and movie stars) that appear elsewhere in the world. Even Presidents Moi and Kenyatta are not depicted in extravagant fashion (or, for that matter, satirically) through expanded and enhanced photographs. The public projection of individual likenesses is restrained and even guarded, which seems to correspond to the subdued, almost iconic portrayal of officials in television and radio news broadcasts. The newspapers follow suit, at least with the major officials.

Photography as a public sign-making practice is confined to the work of a few picture takers who position themselves on the lawn before the municipal building or near the post office. They are like others of their trade from Moscow to Jakarta, though they do not risk taking a photo of a prospect on the street and then trying to sell a print as others do elsewhere. Several have folding signboards covered with color snapshots they have taken of families and couples, who commonly buy the pictures to memorialize a trip to the city.

The equipment of the photo fundi is a name-brand 35mm single-lens-reflex camera fitted with a normal lens. He is limited to snapshots without the panoramic views, special effects, or neutral background permitted by studio cameras and versatile lenses. The limitation is economic. Just as a shoemaker will not purchase a set of intricate leather-working instruments when a knife and a shave will do, the photographer can't risk spending a year's wages on a special lens or filter when he might need the money to maintain his working camera. It is not easy to prove that it is the economics of photography that determines the photographic representation, but most images are of the same sort: full-figured, posed, formal, and static. Kenyans are so used to being photographic subjects (perhaps dating from colonial times) that even their own photographs conform to a tradition of family photography that has the same look everywhere it is practiced.

These Kenyan conventions of photography pose a moral dilemma for a photographer of Kenyan technology since it is impossible to photograph an artisan with his knowledge and not have him pose. On the other hand, this fixed sense of what a photograph should be, which seems to be a subcategory of what a sign should be, helps the public photographer because he knows exactly what his clients want, and he does not need a variety of equipment to achieve it. He need only claim the setting where people want to have their pictures taken.

The taking of the photo completes the photographer's sign semiotically but not technologically. He needs to have his film developed, and he does not undertake that himself. Polaroid cameras and film are not available in Eldoret. The only way to have film developed soon enough to gratify clients is at one of the establishments, all Asian-owned, that feature automatic developing. The photo fundi can have his color prints within two hours. He must, however, be able to pay for the processing when he orders the prints. Yet he cannot collect his fee from the subject until he hands over the finished prints, and even then only when they appear to be satisfactory.

The photo fundi is caught between two technologies: the social technology of his picture taking and the firm productive technology of the developing facilities. That this sign making as a social use of technology is conditioned by economic relations is obvious from the two classes of people involved. Once again, Asian capital makes available a technology that Kenyans use and pay for in small ways. The photo fundi's clients cannot afford a camera, an entire roll of film, and developing to take a snapshot of their visit to the city; the photo fundi cannot afford his own developing apparatus. It is an ascending pyramid of equipment and service. In order to produce the photograph, however, the fundi is the one who must take the risk and suspend himself between developer and customer. This perilous economy may be one reason why there are only a few public photographers who have defined their task and materials very narrowly. Two of the photo shops can arrange to have photos taken for customers who do not wish to use the services of the public photographers, but custom and scarcity have not encouraged the formation of photo studios or the use of plate cameras.

For all the eclectic energy of public sign making, and the variety of technologies that contribute to the Eldoret signscape, there is a singular lack of spontaneous engagement with civic spaces. There is, for instance, no graffiti at all: not on the walls of buildings exposed to the open, not inside public lavatories, not on vehicles, nor in any of the other places where it is usually found. The effulgent, politically and/or religiously impassioned painted graffiti covering entire building faces in South Indian, Egyptian, and Mexican cities, for example, is nowhere to be seen. The cultivated bathroom graffiti of colleges and their towns is also absent, even from the university and its precincts. Obviously, the people of Eldoret do not lack the passion, humor, or technology to engage in even modest acts of expressive defacement, yet such acts seem to be singularly absent.

While asking a negative question like this may be begging the question—Must the *absence* of graffiti be explained?—it is worth pursuing a short distance. Eldoret is in its own way an "incessant city," active around the clock, though not in the same way as New York or Tokyo. The ceaselessness of Eldoret doesn't come from bright lights, busy traffic, and round-the-clock entertainment: smart guides to Kenya classify it as a very dull place in implicit comparison with Soho, the Ginza, or even parts of Nairobi. Only the hotel restaurants are open after 7:00 P.M.; the last showing at the video parlor is 6:30 P.M. It is not in its activity that Eldoret is ceaseless, but in its watching.

There is no place in the city where one can act unobserved for any period of time. All spaces are either in use or closed and monitored. Many of the shops downtown actually front *biashara* (business) residences with large internal courtyards and resident populations. There are many "unofficial" residents who rent no quarters and don't even occupy the fixed structures of squatters. A large number of askaris guard stores and building sites, which also are secured by construction workers living in corrugated huts on the job site. I know of one askari who settled down years ago as a worker on the building he now guards.

With so many watchers, it is impossible to do anything that might affect the character of the urban space without someone remarking it and challenging the act. If it is a partisan sign, political or religious, the challenge will be sharp. Spray paints might give the edge, as they have in New York and Los Angeles, but they aren't available.

Other reasons for the lack of graffiti have to do with the nature of sign making. A sign is a public statement, and it had best have force that cannot be resisted. The only political signs in town are a large, colored metal KANU sign directly in front of the municipal building, another on the outskirts, and posters on the KANU party headquarters. There are constituencies for the predominantly Luo FORD-A (Forum of Rural Democracy) party (now split into A and B sections) and the Kikuyu DP (Democratic Party), but they have not attempted to erect signs or set up headquarters, although one shoemaker sits nestled in a corner where he has written in chalk, "Vote for Kibaki" (the DP candidate). As long as he guards it, it will remain. For the rest, the burnings and trashings that opposition party headquarters have suffered in strong KANU areas are a warning against attempting signs and graffiti. The religious crusade posters are pasted down rapidly, but ripped away just as fast; it is only people's zeal that makes them reappear, and perhaps disappear as well.

But Eldoret does have an artificial graffiti, located exactly where the signs are. Near election time, "Vote for Moi" (the president and head of the ruling KANU party) was seen painted in various colors on park benches and stone walls around the city. Nowhere did it interfere with a commercial or governmental sign. The graffiti seemed simply to be the usual painted signs with the added element of informality, so you could be seen looking at them. However, this contrived official graffiti only made the absence of genuine graffiti more obvious.

When the force of the regard meets the force of the sign, there is identity and commitment. Even if someone did succeed in scrawling "Vote for Matiba" or "Jesus is King" across the front of the police station (to invent extreme examples), anyone seen looking at it would be deemed party to the defacement. Signs are made and viewed under a narrow set of social, commercial, and technological circumstances.

Apart from the kinyozi signs and the photos, there are few representational signs in Eldoret. Signs go by quickly on the wheel flaps of minivans and bicycles, which are painted by the same sign makers who do the lettering on the common signs. These are often religious enjoinders or pastoral scenes with a god-fearing message beneath. Even the new Roman Catholic cathedral lacks any statuary or outward representation of the human figure; the old Catholic church had only a single figure of Saint Anthony on a platform over the entrance. One odd full-length figure is pictured on the facade of a nursery school on Moi Avenue: Mickey Mouse in a suit with an Edwardian collar, holding a child mouse by the hand. But this figure has been upstaged by the likeness of Krishna on the architrave over the entrance to the new Hindu temple not far away.

The Radhkrishna Temple, completed and opened in May 1993, replaces the temple that was part of the Patel Center, a Hindu social hall on the other side of Moi Avenue. The pastel-colored knobbed finials of the vihara, or inner temple, are visible over the wall of the facade. However, one's attention is drawn immediately to the entranceway, where a broad lintel carries a brightly colored relief of Krishna playing his flute while attended by an admiring Radha, both flanked by a pair of cows dashing through a lush landscape. Directly below, on the entrance walls, are equally colorful figures of apsarases, winged divinities who hover protectively, while the walls on either side of the massive wooden door carry the figures of Jay and Vijay, the burly, sword-bearing, turbaned guardians of the temple. The reliefs were designed and cast in Nairobi, but painted locally by two Brahman specialists from India. The pastel light of the color and the depiction of human shapes makes the temple face a sign like no other in Eldoret (although a Kenyan sign maker named David assisted the Brahman painters, and his new kinyozi signs now show that influence). Inside, on the ceiling of the main temple, are oil paintings of Hindu divinities in the style of chromolithographs. These brightly colored religious paintings are common in all Hindu communities and also

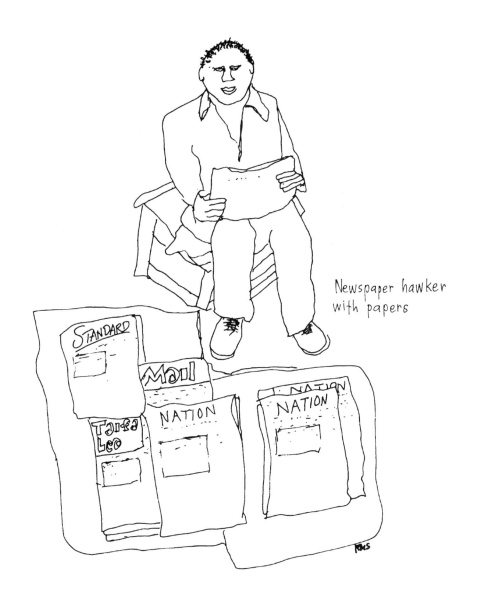

Newspaper hawker
with papers

appear in a series of comic books depicting inspirational stories in Indian as well as English. While the architecture of the Sikh temples and the mosque nearby also distinguishes them from the main of Eldoret buildings, the new Hindu temple is a sign made by and for the Asian community, and also represents the technological dominance of this community.

All of these signs—posters, photos, temple paintings, and language usage itself—are realms of discourse identifying their own distinctiveness with political, economic, and ethnic groups, and achieving their status through a use of technologies. The one realm of discourse that can encompass all of these is newspapers, not produced but distributed and sold throughout Eldoret by men who hawk them in the streets or from stacks on the ground or pavement. In the newspapers are the same affirmations and contests concerning party, language, and sign that are seen in the streets and on the sides of buildings. Thus the newspaper hawkers may be the most powerful sign makers, but because their signs are so ephemeral, perhaps they are also the most vulnerable.

14. The Empty Market

On 17 February 1993, the Eldoret Municipal Council, acting through the police, had the entire outdoor section of the Eldoret downtown market bulldozed. The high-traction, five-meter-blade road leveler, borrowed from a highway construction company, flattened and swept away the collection of tables and booths hurriedly left behind by the hawkers and artisans who had made the place a lively and blazingly colorful center of town life. The town authorities had a different opinion, however, and wanted the people doing business there to move outside the city center. The national newspapers reported little more than these bare facts, but to people living in Eldoret, the events had a strong context of national significance.

A news item the previous week suggested something of this context. A man referred to in the newspapers as a "Kalenjin businessman" was killed in the Huruma Estate, a settlement some four kilometers outside of Eldoret town. The police went on a rampage, hauling men from bars, beating them, and in the end, killing three. Sixty-nine people were imprisoned initially, and twenty more were arrested in the wake of arson in another section of the town. Relatives of the detainees gathered outside the central police station, waiting for news of their kin. The following day, the market was leveled, and armed police became a constant presence on the streets of a subdued Eldoret. Much of the city's typical animation fell back into quiet streets. Matatu activity was stilled. Eldoret seemed like a science-fictional town whose inhabitants' bodies had been taken over by dour aliens.

An editorial in the *Nation* on 20 February 1993 suggested that matters were going badly in Kenya if there were clashes in Eldoret, the chief city of the president's home province and a showcase of the "stability and progress" of his campaign slogan.

Most of the displaced hawkers and artisans are Kikuyu. One rationale for the expulsion even pointed to the use of the market as a harbor for Kikuyu criminals fleeing the police. In what sounds almost comically like a racist stereotype heard from law enforcement officers in multiracial cities, it was said that a Kikuyu could easily lose himself among his or her compatriots in the maze of booths and tables.

Prior to the demolition, police agents circulated through the area advising the hawkers to relocate to K Square, about two kilometers north of the center, off the main road but beside a stadium and closer to Huruma Estate. K Square is indeed a square of buildings around an open space. All of the essentials of a small self-enclosed village are there, including a beverage depot, post office, food shops, and *posho* (maize) mill. A number of woodworking shops that specialize in furniture had established themselves there, and the square had the reputation of being a place to buy furniture at prices lower than in town. Within a few days of the expulsion, hawkers had begun to reestablish themselves in the K Square area, although not within the square itself, but behind the buildings, along a road that borders the square, and in a parking lot beside a school building. If the intention of the expulsion was to force Kikuyu informal businesses to concentrate near an area of Kikuyu lower-income residence, then it was showing signs of success.

The used clothing and plastic goods sellers were in evidence, but there were fewer of them, and instead of spreading their goods out over tables or over the ground as they had done in town, they had them in piles or even on hangers along racks. Some of the technologically most distinctive enterprises did not make the transition. There were no key cutters or cassette tape sellers. The tire repair/processing complex that had occupied an entire corner with its heaps of tractor tires and plank huts had been reduced to smoldering rubble. Within a few days, stacks of tractor tires with men perched on them appeared on the corner of the waste lot opposite, as if waiting to return once more.

On the most superficial level, the demolition of the informal market was just one more skirmish in a battle between two modes of technology: the informal, ephemeral, inventive, and minimally capitalized mode of the small-scale artisan versus the formal, long-lasting, established, and heavily capitalized mode of the businessman. Among those cleared out of the center of town were stamp makers, sign painters, and repair fundi of several varieties. They will be replaced by buildings, probably stores and office buildings.

The hawkers and fundi can practice their trades elsewhere, and others are practicing the same trades out in the streets of Eldoret, but there are fewer of them. The technology is not eliminated, but its personnel are scattered, and its practice curtailed. The technology does bear some attachment to the people, but technology is like language: having a formal structure and a concrete inflection does not exempt it from economic and political influences.

The eradication of the informal market seems to have been related to a number of immediate and long-range developments that themselves give shape to the conflict of technologies and people in Eldoret. In March 1993, an annual Agricultural Society of Kenya (ASK) Fair was scheduled to be held on the Eldoret fairgrounds, just outside the downtown on Kisumu Road. With its pointedly stated theme, "Intensify Rural and Industrial Development," and its demonstrations of farm machinery and "anti-poaching techniques," the fair was designed to be a showcase of KANU's stewardship and of the kinds of advances made during that period. It also obviously was planned to emphasize the goals of the land-aggregating, heavy-technology capitalizing wealth seekers over the small-holders. The president himself was to open the show. To have an array of ramshackle shops in the center of town was less tolerable than ever.

Eldoret was taking on a more respectable look. No fewer than five new shopping centers were nearing completion in different parts of town, including the massive Barn'getuny Center. At the same time, the construction of a system of water channels designed to remove flow from the streets, or at least prevent it from cascading downhill, was nearing completion. The informal market was outdoors, disposed on ground cover and wooden tables, often muddy or dusty. From the viewpoint of the entrepreneurs and municipal officials, it was the antithesis of the indoors, professionalized Eldoret they were trying to create with their new construction.

There was not much question of direct economic competition between the informal market and the new buildings, which would have offices and service firms as well as shops. The competition was over which businesses would take up land in the town center. The goods and services sold in the informal market were used, put-together, shoddy; the goods and services to be sold inside the new centers were upscale and befitting a progressive urban population. The informal market had long coexisted with hardware stores, garages, and new clothing stores in Eldoret, but the new buildings, which were to house a number of formal enterprises under the same roof, seemed to emphasize the polarity of the informal and formal technologies and styles.

This obvious conflict was not, however, what most strongly operated to the exclusion of the hawkers and artisans. It was more fundamentally a conflict between groups, but not *ethnic* groups. It might appear that it was the poor Kikuyu against the rich Asians and their Kalenjin allies, but there were Kikuyu, both men and women, financing, building, and inhabiting the new structures. A number of Kikuyu professionals and businessmen had won seats on the municipal council in the December 1992 election, most of them members of parties in opposition to the ruling KANU party. The expelled hawkers and artisans were Kikuyu, but more importantly, they were participants in the local Kikuyu community, not in the municipal political and commercial life of Eldoret.

While it is a cliché of Western understanding of Africa that tribal loyalties take precedence over all others, the ouster of the informal market ran across ethnic lines and even class lines. There was work for the class compatriots of the informal market people in the construction and maintenance of the new buildings. A welder, whose brother, a key cutter, had been forced to move his business to K Square, might be assembling security windows for the new shopping center on Nairobi Road. The welder could be Kikuyu, Kalenjin, Luhya, or any other. An Asian master electrician could have a Kikuyu apprentice whose brother sold used clothes in the market.

The advent of the new conglomerate buildings and the demise of the open-air artisans in the center of town parallel the introduction of machinery into agriculture on the farms outside Eldoret. In the end, it is the greater capital aggregate that takes precedence. On the farms, the capital is controlled by men and subordinates the women further. In town, the Asians and Kalenjin have more control over the capital aggregate, which sets up the Kikuyu and Luhya to engage themselves as subordinates or face marginalization and exclusion. The capital aggregate is open to anyone with the resources to manage it, and the Asians have the monetary and skill resources, the Kalenjin the territorial and political base. The exclusion of one technological aggregate before the advance of another is the outward manifestation of an economic trend to literally consolidate capital in the form of buildings and enterprises.

For instance, Kalenjin women's groups began looking into the used-clothing business while the Kikuyu dealers were in disarray or without an inventory in center city. They considered moving into the retail gap of this important business because they had the means to provide a supply of goods and the influence to secure a place, probably not outdoors like their displaced competitors. Gaining the edge lay simply in accessing the supply of used clothing shipped to Mombasa from America, Britain, France, and Italy, where it is collected from estates, unclaimed parcels, and other sources from which consumers in these countries will not purchase. Though it is not as stylish as the Italian or French, the American clothing is preferred because it is larger and more likely to fit Kenyan purchasers.

The Kalenjin women planned to go to Mombasa and chase down a shipment, going through the complex formalities required to bid for it, import it, and transport the container to Eldoret. Once they had taken possession, they could retail the individual sacks of clothing to sellers. If they were successful in usurping the entrance point of the commodity path, they were confident they could also seize an advantage in sales and displace the Kikuyu women. This economic conflict between women, which paralleled the expulsion of the predominantly male artisans, came after the women had already been displaced by ethnic conflicts and impoverished by gender conflicts. Again, those who controlled the capital aggregate were able to seek advantage of a technology developing in the area: direct shipment of containers to the depot.

An earlier phase of this same development was in the emergence of supermarkets in Eldoret, which was also a technological manifestation of economic process that could be marked as ethnic. The outdoor fruit and vegetable market was one of the earliest features of Eldoret as a community. Farmers from the periphery brought their products into town to sell. The locus of the market shifted over the years from an indefinite place near a crossroads and beside the river, to a paved area with concrete islands, to a designed, roofed, and enclosed market uphill from the original and some distance away.

The municipal council granted licenses to sell produce in particular numbered stations, but commonly used commodities such as sugar, flours, coffee, tea, and canned vegetables were not sold in the municipal market. These were stocked by general merchandise stores along the streets of the downtown. These stores also carried cloth, hardware, and utensils on a basis of availability and profitability. Because their stock was not as perishable as the fruits and vegetables of the market, storekeepers could not only maintain a larger inventory but also keep it for longer periods to take advantage of rising prices. Asian merchants spe-

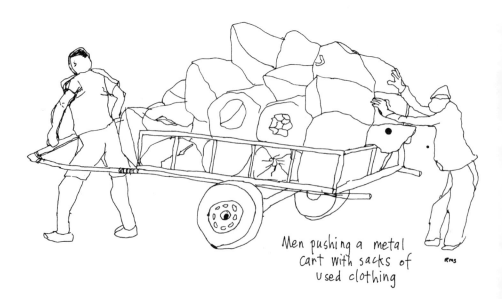

Men pushing a metal
cart with sacks of
used clothing

cialized in such stock-engineered supply tracks and storage facilities to improve their business. Their enterprise dictated having at their disposal a greater capital at any one time than did their counterparts in the outdoor food market.

Supermarkets were simply the general merchandise stores that specialized in food. To this end, the Asian merchants who controlled the supermarkets invested in refrigeration and bagging technologies that would not have given their outdoor market operators any economic advantage. By being able to stock ice creams and cold bottled sodas, the supermarket added a sector of the market that could not be served elsewhere. And by being able to seal in plastic bags everything from bulk shipped rice and sugar to dates and a variety of earth chewed by pregnant Kenyan (and not Asian) women, the Asian supermarket owners broadened their stock once more. Even with refrigeration, the supermarkets avoided carrying fresh produce, which would create supply and transport problems that would reduce profits.

Thus two economically and technologically distinct modes of foodstuff selling arose in Eldoret. The distinction even took on a cast of structural differentiation in which the "market" foods belonged to a set of categories discernable from the supermarket foods. When a "new" food, boxed fruit juices, was introduced into the Eldoret area from a deftly concealed South African producer, it was predictable that the supermarkets and not the outdoor market would offer them. Foods that might fit into the market (unpackaged) and supermarket (packaged) categories, such as eggs, are sold in both places, but the chickens that lay the eggs are strictly an outdoor item. Apples and other products imported from South Africa (during apartheid), unlike ginger imported from Zanzibar, have probably become supermarket items because the Asian supermarket owners could get a high ("imported") price for them.

Two indoor markets sell fresh produce in Eldoret, but it is significant that they are both owned and operated by Kenyans. Although they do employ refrigeration technology, they do not repackage goods or sell any of the hard (canned or bottled) goods offered by the supermarkets. The produce they sell is more specialized and of a higher quality than what is typically sold outside. They fill a niche between market and supermarket.

Even with their stock of imported wines and fruit juices, these produce stores are more like ambitious market tables than supermarkets.

The market, because it is a compound of small-scale individual enterprises with consensual pricing and limited negotiating, can always provide a model for sellers who defy municipal regulation and take to the streets, selling their goods wherever they can, asking higher prices for their bananas if they manage to be close to transport stops. Since they represent the essence of the difference between market and supermarket (and the oldest form of food selling in Eldoret), these freelancers are the greatest threat to settled, fee-paying food sellers. Joining them are a range of street food sellers who offer snacks that are usually only available in restaurants, if at all: balls of fat coated with sesame seeds, samosas (fried dough pockets with meat or vegetable filling), and sausages. These were among the hawkers eliminated by the council's sweep. The key cutters, metalworkers, rubber fundi, and other artisans driven out of the center of town stand in about the same relation to other formal enterprises on a different scale and are differently capitalized, usually by Asians. The consolidating commerce and technology of downtown Eldoret found itself opposed in many senses by these people and their practices, and expressed its dominance by eliminating them

Battles between police or municipal askaris and the hawkers and artisans have been a feature of Nairobi municipal life for some years. The informal operators set themselves up on a piece of land owned by the city and do their work unmolested until the land is required for building, or there are complaints from more formally constituted competitors. Around the time the Eldoret expulsion took place, there was another series of battles over land between hawkers-artisans and police-askaris. The new mayor of Nairobi, Steven Mwangi, the first mayor in many years to be elected by the city council and not appointed by the central government, resolved to "clean up" the city, and he actually was photographed taking a shovel to one of the many heaps of refuse that were the subject of much complaint. His deputy mayor, in suit and tie, less convincingly pushed a refuse-filled wheelbarrow. This literal cleaning, however, acquired an ominous resonance when metaphorically extended to include the elimination of hawkers and artisans from municipal land, and the word "cleansing" was used to describe the operation.

A similar rhetoric was used by the Eldoret Municipal Council, although the reporter who described the action in a supplement to the daily *Nation* on the Eldoret ASK show unconsciously expressed a double meaning:

> The administration has set aside enough land for investors who are willing to put up industrial concerns in the town.
>
> Two weeks ago, the council evicted over 2,000 open-air hawkers operating outside the main municipal market, thus making the town look shabby and congested.
>
> However, the council managed to accommodate the displaced hawkers—second-hand tire dealers, clothes sellers, lock-smiths and many others—at the Eldoret West Market and at the jua kali sheds along the banks of River Sosiani. (5 March 1993, p. 10)

(The phrasing of the sentence beginning "Two weeks ago" makes it sound as if the eviction, not the hawkers, made the town look shabby and congested.)

In this way, the refugees returned to the stony river that gave Eldoret its name.

However, a look about the town one month after the eviction showed that a simple bilateral interpretation of the eviction might be premature. Indeed the major opposition politician Kenneth Matiba (FORD-A party) may have been trying to capitalize on the discontent by scheduling a rally at Huruma Stadium, and letting it be canceled by the government. But the same enterprises as before were operating in their new locations, only more neatly. The cleaning had meant ordering more than exclusion. On Ngala and Oginga Odinga streets, artisans and hawkers had consolidated their stock and erected tight wooden booths with signs for its display. The Sosia River booths at the foot of Oginga Odinga Street had been extended and enclosed from a small jua kali metalworking area to a collection of contiguous artisan, hawker, and kinyozi sheds, including three of the locksmiths sent off from the market area, and a new business, The Eldoret Coffin Shop, later renamed The Eldoret Coffin and Furniture Shop.

Even the matatus were obeying what seemed to be a general enjoinder to order by collecting their passengers within the matatu park that had been set aside in the old market near the river, and not on the street outside. The KCC matatu had disappeared from the road beside the Agip station and was instead waiting inside the station lot.

Mwangi, the locksmith whose key cutting was described earlier, had invested in a small free-standing enclosure with a table in front to hold the assortment of locks and hasps that he used to spread on the ground in the old marketplace. While in that location, he did not need to set up a sign since his business and wares were clearly visible, but in the new place, he erected two signs, one on a tree beside the road and another above his shop. They both indicated his key- and rubber stamp–cutting skills, which the change of location had not affected. However, the new place was shaded and darker than his former location in the bright sun, and he complained about the difficulty focusing on the keys and instruments, and the slow flow of customers, who could no longer simply stop on their way to the market but had to make a detour. Still, he was pleased that his right to do business in the space was more or less assured. This sentiment was not universal among the displaced.

The principle that had been defeated in the "cleansing" operation was not artisanship or minimally capitalized enterprise but the capacity to conduct this activity in the open, in a crowded, visibly public space, which had become defined as "shabby" in the official parlance. The switch in Eldoret technology was not in materials and workmanship, but in their exposure. In a time when the enclosures of major businesses in Eldoret were growing more ornate, with several stories of brickwork instead of the plain single-story, painted plaster wall, the informal enterprises were expected to move up a notch of formality and at least surround themselves with wooden walls. The small businesses were made into units separate from each other and readily accessible to the regulatory authority of the municipality. The old informal market may not have been a single organism made of cooperatively competing social units, but it was difficult to enter it and make contact with only one type of business. In the more orderly arrangement, this became possible. There was no longer a mob gathered doing business on public land in the center of the city. They were individuals running single businesses. By forcing the artisans to take their places within the rigid urban grid, the businessmen and politicians succeeded in "cleansing" Eldoret.

For a time, a madman walked the streets and roads of Eldoret. He was completely naked, and he walked endlessly straight ahead, not looking at anyone or anything, yet certainly conscious at least of his direction and not so crazed that he disregarded traffic or sunken road shoulders. He was stripped of everything except his motion, and that motion was absolute. It was said that he might strike and batter women he encountered, and that may be why he eventually disappeared. As remarkable as his persistence during the month or so that he was in the area was the tolerance of the passing public. He was not molested or spirited away even though his route took him past the hospitals and into town. Possibly it was because he walked with definition and purpose like everyone else along the accepted routes.

There was also a woman lunatic who for a while stood and sang songs in Samburu in the middle of traffic downtown. She was clad in a dusty old dress and was known to sleep in among the trees near the nursing home, before the trees were cut down. She rose in the morning, took her position, and began to sing. The cars and trucks made their way around her when she stood in the road, but she did that rarely, preferring the roadside.

A man with legs withered by infant polio made his way through the downtown in his own unique manner. He wore a large black shoe on his left foot, which he advanced with each forward motion. He carried his whole body close to the ground with the help of a single stout staff. With the left leg, bent completely at the knee, the man placed the shoe, and he brought his right leg, which was twisted left at the thigh, forward and rested his knee on the shoe for balance as the whole man pressed ahead by one more step.

These people, like others in Eldoret, organized the resources available to them to make the ways they wished. With the help of the potential of their own bodies, they maintain a practice both as individuals and as members of groups. Being an individual and a group member *is* a practice in human realms.

This study doesn't go through a list of institutions, each serving an essential function. There is no section on the commissary, the schools, or the churches, each of which is an element in the technological whole of the town and has its own array of technologies and their uses. The commissary has a physical structure, a matrix of numbered locations, roofed over, accessible by a looping roadway, and surrounded by a chain-link fence. Fruits, vegetables, grains, spices, and chickens are packaged and transported to this place, where they are displayed and sold by men and women to customers who transport, store, prepare, and consume them. The market is crisscrossed by a number of the lines of supply and sale with angle and momentum traced out here. The classical functioning institution that social scientists find a useful benchmark even when they reject functional theory shows in outline only. The schools are like the churches, which in turn are like the market, only because the same people are involved.

The functional image of a society is very tempting to a student of technology in context because the mechanical analogy—that society works like a machine—is always potential in any analysis. If the society works like a machine, then the culture must be the technique of its operation. At the risk of seeming self-contradictory, in individual passages I have tried to show that Eldoret does not work like a machine, even a malfunctioning machine. But it would be disingenuous to assert that I am a plain realist trying to show things exactly as they are with no suggestion of pattern. There clearly are mechanisms and techniques, and there clearly are human varieties—of gender, ethnicity, and training—that have something to do with the operation of the mechanisms and techniques.

This conclusion most readily becomes a series of associations: men work most of the heavy tools; Asians have priority in management; specifically trained fundi do most of the handiwork. This is merely the way things are in Eldoret. There is nothing about tools that makes them male, or about management that makes it Asian. The human and technological essences are associated with each other by accident, in a manner that seems fundamental because it has a history, and has come to seem "right" cognitively even to one who does not belong to the community.

It has been part of the task of this study to project that sense of the rightness of certain arrangements without arguing for their transcendental truth. The control exercised over the flow of various fluids is not the nature of those fluids but an attempt to show them as controlled. There is no special water or traffic for Eldoret, though it can appear that way with enough description. The observer of technology always hovers between these two forms of essentialism, that of the group-person-place and that of large abstractions (economy, education, religion).

This study underlines the importance of history, economy, and cognition, to name just three influences, in the workings of technology. Things do not merely function even when they can be described exhaustively as such. An oxyacetylene blowpipe does not need a description of its operator's training and social position to cut a sheet of metal. Yet it *does* cut metal under those circumstances, and they may be more specific than functionalism projects. The metal may actually not be cut anywhere in the absence of cultural specifics. Eldoret may be doing what it does in ways far more peculiar to itself than the outward motions of its devices cause an observer to believe.

This is not a brief for a radical particularism that finds a technology's working only with these people in this place. That easily turns into exoticism, interested only in what can be shown to be peculiar to this setting; or cultural reductionism, ignoring the mechanical workings. This study is an invitation to consider the possibilities created by having the essentialist and the particularist extremes ready and waiting.

Years ago, I demonstrated with an array of historical and ethnographic evidence that a single ballad had originated in the description of a historical event in a single New England community, only to uncover evidence shortly after the publication of the study that indicated the same ballad had originated in another community as well, and another, and another. It turned out to be a migratory legend that reproduced an authenticity of beginning everywhere it was known. So history and the other forms of evidence can be spuriously particular while in fact essential, and yet look back to a particular moment just the same. Particularism and essentialism do not exhaust description; a single piece of evidence can be an emergent generalization, which in turn is becoming an example of the moment.

A common form in Eldoret is the paper nut cone. Hawkers, paper sellers, and small children set up beside the street with plastic tubs in which these cones of uniform size fan from where their apices meet in the center, forming several layers of circle. A cone costs only two or three shillings. A passerby pays the seller, takes a cone, tears off the circle end, pours the nuts into his mouth and continues, discarding the paper. Flattened rays of newspaper, along with bottle caps and maize cobs, are the commonest litter of Eldoret streets.

At the beginning of the day, a nut seller buys a quantity of roasted, salted, ground peanuts in one of the shops. He or she then tears unfolded newspaper sections into quarters (cloth is cut in about the same way in fabric stores), places one on a flat surface, rolls it together in an arc preserving the point in one end, feeds a palmful of nuts into the open end, folds over the flaps, then adds the completed cone to the arrangement. It is a good stacking form, like the tetrahedral packets in which fresh milk is sold, and it is a good food-conveying form, superior to the rectangular containers that spill. And it is a good penny capitalist form, keeping cost and price down while granting enough of a profit margin to justify perpetuating the business. Nut cones are for sale in many Kenyan towns and cities: the materials are available everywhere, and the customers recognize them. But why do they take this form?

It would be awkward to try to sell loose nuts to customers and always provide equal portions while quelling the universal concerns over food contamination. The cones' neatness provides assurance of honesty, and freedom from foreign matter. They can be carried a distance, and given to a child or a friend with no apprehensions aroused. In the absence of a street bread like the batura of India or the semit of the Near East, the nut cones are ready carbohydrates.

But is this technology determined by material factors alone? Does the geometry of the cone in the circle have a special appeal that made this form prominent instead of others using the same materials? Or are there conditions, material or aesthetic, that exercise a determining force? Are the cones a member in a larger structure?

The first computer school opened in Eldoret in 1992, on an upper floor of College House, above the Elgon View Commercial College. In a detailed advertisement in the first issue of the Eldoret *Weekly News*, the principal of the college explained that computer training is a valuable asset in employment and advanced education. The college's roster of courses published in the same issue affirmed that orientation: computer basics, Lotus, Wordperfect 5.1, desktop publishing. Photographs showed rows of computers attended by serious students, and a few letters from children attesting to the interest and value of computers. The courses were rather expensive by the standard of commercial courses. Shortly thereafter, the Eldoret *Weekly News* ceased to be published, the small posters for the computer school posted around town faded away, and the computer school itself was no longer to be found in its advertised location. The woman who operated it had moved the school to a large house overlooking the golf course.

I conclude without a conclusion. While this project was originally framed as an ethnographic study, it has lost those trappings with accumulation of experience. I still live in Eldoret and have a resident's constellation of qualms and enthusiasms. Though I will leave before long, I do not want to engineer a closure of the subject just because I will no longer be here to look at it, nor do I want to pretend still to be looking while far away.

Appendix 1: Hitting Pictures

Looking at a photograph of the Krupp steelworks, Bertolt Brecht remarked that he could see nothing of the industry's social and economic organization. Looking at a photograph of herself, a Kenyan knows a great deal about the organization of the photographer's enterprise. She knows that this is not an innocent, neutral act, that it at least means pictures shown to relatives, and perhaps printed in a newspaper or book.

She also knows that some money might come to the photographer for the picture, which she will never share. Of course, she is aware of the price of a camera, film, and though she may not distinguish developing the film from making the prints, she knows that additional money is required. She knows how much it costs to have her photo taken by one of the public photographers around the post office. So she may be willing to let an mzungu take a photo of her in exchange for a print. She might want to know what's going to happen to the negative, and refuse permission to have it in a book about Kenya. And if she agrees to a photo, it is not going to be a spontaneous unposed shot of her at work. She will decide on her pose and on her dress at the time of the photograph. It is as if the Krupp steelworks knew Brecht was going to be looking at their photograph and determined to paint itself with outlines intended to show the organization it wanted him to see.

Photography, basically the same technology, had some of the same uses in Brecht's Germany as it does in Kenya today. It is a medium of family portraiture and scene-recording, of journalistic record, of advertising, and of remembering the dead and gone. The uses are well known to Kenyans today and condition their response when they are asked for a photograph. All of the photographs that I intended to include in this book were taken with the knowledge and cooperation of the people photographed. Almost always, I had agreed in advance to give the person(s) photographed a copy of the photo, and often I gave them, at their request, some *chai*—five, ten, or twenty shillings. I simply set the camera and snapped the shutter and went through the round of having the film developed and the prints made. I became acquainted with the darkroom man at Eldo Snaps, a Kenyan employed as usual by Asians, and he did the best he could with both the film and the prints despite depleted solutions, poor temperature control, and outdated paper.

The people to whom I gave the photos were usually delighted with the result because it was of a pose they had made and would cost them at least twenty-five shillings from a street photographer. I thought initially that the black-and-white format would be cause for dissatisfaction, but it proved the opposite because it looked like a newspaper picture in size, and alas, in texture. My antics trying to get the right angle and lighting for the picture the people had set were always amusing, provoking a commentary in Sheng, or a vernacular, and often drawing a jokey crowd. The size of the Nikon with its antiquated motor drive and protruding lens more than once invited obscene commentary in a language I was not supposed to understand. (Even street people don't insult someone in his hearing.) This amusement was often offset by a desire to look one's best for the camera, which meant not to be caught smiling or playing. I even was led to conclude that if they can manage the scene as they want, many Kenyans will pose for their own funerary portraits, projecting a seriousness and sobriety that will carry them into eternity.

I initially failed to appreciate this timeless quality of photography. I was educated by encountering people whom I had photographed a month earlier and not seen since, because they had been away, asking for their pictures. I took to carrying the undelivered copies with me whenever I walked in town, and I always met their owners sooner or later.

It was irresistible at times just to take a photograph and announce my presence later, because the picture would have dissolved had I made known my intention. Monitoring was such that this was not often possible. Once I produced the camera and began adjusting it, wondering if I shouldn't stick with a fully automated little camera for these attempts, my intended subjects spotted me and began negotiations or signaled that they did not want a picture taken. There was a feeling that if I was simply trying to take a picture of an empty street or a wall with drawings, I was acting crazy, a wasteful mzungu, and "Why not photograph me?" I met one man, a back-alley shopkeeper and fence, who assumed when I took some photos of a broken drain that I was taking his picture, even though he was about twenty meters down the alley and inside a car. When I assured him I was taking pictures of the pipe, he asked me why, and I really didn't have a satisfactory answer. He relented when I agreed to come and take his picture when he could be more picturesquely accoutered.

Photographs in an ethnographic text have the metatextual function of displaying the writer/photographer's rapport with the people, and thus his or her competence to compose the text. Strong images of people who clearly trust the photographer make for a strong description and suggest the integrity of the analysis. They also calm, if not put to rest, suspicions of exploitation. It is even possible to build an ethnography out of such photos and let the writing be only a reflection, as in John Berger's books. But I think that this sort of image may be demanded by Europeans and Americans inundated with graphics and needing a jolt to fall into the picture. Instead of this culture-bound strategy, I chose another culture-bound strategy, of showing the pictures that the people themselves want, which they try to fashion in the camera for their own purposes. The attitude may be illustrated best by photos I took of the boy Keiya, who always adopted a karate pose. That is how he wanted to be seen at the moment of his life when he was making wheeled toys.

The images are in the triangle formed by the technology being illustrated, the technology of the camera, and the person. People and technology are most fully intermingled in the photographs that were "hit" (*piga*), not taken, but whether taking or hitting them, the process was revealing about the poetics of technology in Eldoret.

There are no photographs in the text because local developing of black-and-white negatives with depleted solutions produced negatives of substandard quality (itself another poetics). The photographs did serve as the basis for some of the drawings, which I made using a technical drafting pen on coarse drafting paper, usually while the subject watched. Several times the person drawn wanted to draw me or a friend afterwards, which results they always kept. The refinements required to handle a technical pen entertained the Kenyan users greatly: "the little point," the cassette seller called it, quoting a popular song.

Appendix 2: Making Maps

The map included in this text is based on the 1:10,000 scale map published by the Ministry of Physical Planning office in Eldoret. There is a map of the Eldoret area on the 1:50,000 scale available (or not) from the National Cartography office in Nairobi. No general guide maps or tourist maps of Eldoret have been published except for a partial schematic map of the downtown in Geoff Crowther's *Lonely Planet Guide to Kenya*. I asked children and adults, both Kenyans and Europeans, to draw maps of Eldoret and found the most amazing discrepancies in perceptions of the place, not always in keeping with the expected age, gender, class differences—but that is another study.

The map included here in effect delineates the official conception of Eldoret land: how it is parceled out and numbered in the registry of ownership. In tracing this map, I eliminated the numbered divisions within blocks and emphasized the layout that reveals the roads and passageways. Since the 1980 map was, as indicated in the text, a planning map, a number of streets marked on the map did not yet exist in 1994 and were thus eliminated on the tracing.

In Kenya, maps are produced by central authorities for political purposes. This is true elsewhere, but elsewhere people often have the means to produce their own rival maps, and any map therefore is a proposal, not a fiat. I hope that this map suggests that the cartographic process in Eldoret is related to the ongoing dispute over land ownership and development.

The tracing also eliminates contour lines from the original map, while it names things and places not named on that map. This is still not an

Eldoret that most of the people who live there would recognize. This is a map for politicians, landowners, and automobile drivers, which most people in Eldoret are not.

Notes

1. THE MILKMAN

1. *Wazungu* is a Swahili word that generally refers to white foreigners of European origin. The word is the animate class plural of *mzungu,* a noun derived from a verb meaning "to astound." Wazungu are "wonders," though not always in the positive sense. In some ways, the word resembles "gringo" of Latin America or "saipp" of South India.

2. Turkanas are people of eastern Nilotic origin who have lived a pastoral life in northeast Kenya for many generations. The degradation of the environment, progressive desertification, and sociopolitical turmoil have driven many to the south in search of livelihood. The word "Turkana" is virtually a generic label for a guard in Eldoret, much as "Gurkha" is in parts of India. Turkanas are stereotyped as reliable, keen-sighted, and omnivorous.

3. *Askari* is the Swahili word for "soldier," but it is used for any security guard. Like a few other words, it has entered Kenyan English to designate a category of employment characteristically serving the wealthy English speakers who come to Kenya and can afford to employ guards, and has then been borrowed back into Swahili with that meaning. There are now other words in Swahili for soldiers and police.

4. The Bukusu are the largest subgroup of the Luhya people, mainly distinguished from the other Luhya subgroups (the Maragoli and others) by area of residence (though urbanization is clouding this), separate management of male circumcision and other cohort rituals, and perhaps by language.

2. WHEELED TOYS

1. There are at least five of these worker settlements which began as low-grade housing for workers in Raymonds, Ken-Knit, Raiply, CPC EATEC and other factories. They have all grown beyond their original housing stock through the

construction of "informal" shelters by refugees. The more removed settlements are on the increase as refugees arrive, and are centers of much "informal" economic and political activity.

4. CHARCOAL

1. *Makaa* is derived from the verb *kukaa,* "to sit, stay, or remain." It is a plural noun, "the remains" apparently of wood burned by fire. The same verb is the commonest way of asking "Where do you live?"—*Unakaa wapi?* in Swahili—which may be the basis for the question being phrased "Where do you stay?" in Kenyan English.

6. INERTIAL BALANCE

1. People do not run through crowded downtowns in Kenya possibly because a runner will be perceived as fleeing pursuers. They do run on the open road, and of course, Kenya has regularly fielded championship running teams in international competitions. The environmentally cultivated necessity of strong pedal balance can account for this success more readily than biology.

2. When women finally did begin to appear on the roads of Eldoret riding bicycles, and giving rides to men, they were students studying to become nurses and doctors. The students had received the bicycles as gifts from a Swedish aid organization to serve as inexpensive transport to classes, and market women did not wait long before making their own attempts to challenge the male pedal-transport monopoly.

3. The name "Sheng" is commonly derived from *Swahili + English,* where the initial sibilant "s" becomes a stylish palatal "sh." It is more a speech attitude than a coherent language: as Olinde (1986) shows, it differs even from one housing project to another in Nairobi, and certainly from one city or region to another. A *Sheng Dictionary* (Moga and Fee 1993), sold only at newsstands in Nairobi, may be a sign of beginning standardization, but touts and hawkers will never surrender their interlingual improvisation, which requires that their hearers know Swahili, English, and other languages.

8. THE FUNDI COMPLEX

1. The Swahili noun *fundi* is derived from the verb *funda,* which means "to instruct, but esp. of household or tribal instruction as distinct from instruction

given in school" (Johnson 1967:103). *Fundisha,* "do the work of a fundi," is an intensive of the same verb; *jifundisha,* the reflexive, means "learn." Like Arabic, which is not a related language but a strong influence, Swahili transmutes verbal roots into a wealth of nouns, adjectives, and other verbs.

2. The emergence of Kenyan advertising (as opposed to repetition of international imagery) has been tied to the development of a mass market for domestic and automotive goods, the increasing availability of broadcast and print media, and the growth of a cadre of commercial artists and marketing specialists in the cities. The "Chinese medicine" campaign developed for Marshall's Motors, and the "IT" insecticide campaign for Johnson and Johnson in 1993 both had distinctly Kenyan features.

9. TEAMWORK AND MANAGEMENT

1. The field of communication in an urban area like Eldoret is more a matter of social than of mechanical technology. This can easily remain obscure for someone used to ready telephone, automobile, and radio access, but it explains why the road is always lined with people when a presidential motorcade is in the vicinity, even if it was not announced in print or broadcast media, and why someone walking behind you on the path can be speaking aloud and not to him or herself but to a friend or relative some distance away.

2. The institution of the auto/mechanical junkyard with its vast uncataloged supply of parts has not become established in Kenya simply because the agglomeration of parts represented by an entire vehicle is much better kept running as long as it can be. Even a demolished vehicle is a collection of materials with a myriad of uses; hence derelicts are seldom seen along the roads or in the yards and fields.

Bibliography

Abu-Lughod, Janet. 1961. Migrant Adjustment to City Life: The Egyptian Case. *American Journal of Sociology* 67: 22–32.

Agnew, Clive, and Ewan Anderson. 1992. *Water Resources in Arid Realms*. London: Routledge.

Ahmed, Iftikhar, ed. 1985. *Technology and Rural Women*. London: Allen and Unwin.

Bagshawe, A. F., G. Maina, and E. N. Mungola, eds. 1974. *The Use and Abuse of Drugs and Chemicals in Tropical Africa*. Nairobi: East Africa Literature Bureau.

Basalla, George. 1988. *The Evolution of Technology*. Cambridge: Cambridge University Press.

Bijker, W. B., T. P. Hughes, and Trevor Pinch. 1987. *The Social Construction of Technological Systems*. Cambridge, Mass.: MIT Press.

Boserup, Esther. 1970. *Women and Economic Development*. London: Allen and Unwin.

Bromley, Ray, and Chris Gerry, eds. 1979. *Casual Work and Poverty in Third World Cities*. Chichester: John Wiley.

Bujra, Janet. 1992. Ethnicity and Class: The Case of East African "Asians." Pp. 347–61 in *Poverty and Development in the 1990's*, Tim Allen and Alan Thomas, eds. Oxford: Oxford University Press.

Carey-Jones, N. S. 1972. The Decolonization of the White Highlands of Kenya. Pp. 268–83 in *People and Land in Africa South of the Sahara*, R. Mansell Prothero, ed. New York: Oxford University Press.

Carr, Marilyn. 1985. *The AT Reader: Theory and Practice in Appropriate Technology*. London: Intermediate Technology Publications.

Chick, Garry E., and John M. Roberts. 1987. Lathe Craft: A Study in "Part" Appreciation. *Human Organization* 46 (4): 305–17.

Cole, Michael, and Sylvia Scribner. 1974. *Culture and Thought: A Psychological Introduction*. New York: John Wiley and Sons.

Dangerfield, Bernard, ed. 1983. *Water Supply and Sanitation in Developing Countries*. London: The Institution of Water Engineers and Scientists.

Dimmendaal, Gerrit. 1989. On Language Death in Eastern Africa. Pp. 13–31 in *Investigating Obsolescence: Studies in Language Contraction and Death*, Nancy C. Dorian, ed. Cambridge: Cambridge University Press.

Douglas, Ian. 1983. *The Urban Environment*. London: Edward Arnold.

Dutto, Carl A. 1975. *Nyeri Townsmen: Kenya*. Kampala: East African Literature Bureau.

Elmer, L. A. 1943. The Kikuyu Method of Burning Charcoal. *East African Agricultural Journal* 9: 14.

Ewen, Stewart. 1976. *Captains of Consciousness: Advertising and the Social Origins of Consumer Culture*. New York: McGraw-Hill.

Fadel, M. Sallam. 1979. Energy Supply in East Africa. Pp. 5–21 in *Energy Resources in East Africa: Proceedings of the 12th Annual Symposium of the East African Academy, August 1976*. C. P. M. Khamala and John B. Castelino, eds. Nairobi: Kenya National Academy for the Advancement of Arts and Sciences.

Feldman, Rijah. 1984. Women's Groups and Women's Subordination. *Review of African Political Economy* 27/28: 67–85.

Foley, Gerald. 1986. *Charcoal Making in Developing Countries*. Energy Information Programme: Technical Report No. 5. London: International Institute for Environment and Development.

Foley, Gerald, Patricia Moss, and Lloyd Timberlake. 1984. *Stoves and Trees*. London: International Institute for Environment and Development.

Geofrey, E. M., and G. C. M. Mutiso. 1979. *Politics, Economics and Technical Training: A Kenyan Case Study*. Nairobi: Kenya Literature Bureau.

Gitelman, Lisa. 1992. Negotiating a Vocabulary for Urban Infrastructure: Or, The WPA Meets Teenage Mutant Ninja Turtles. *Journal of American Studies* 26(2): 147–58.

Grillo, R. D. 1973. *African Railwaymen: Solidarity and Opposition in an East African Labor Force*. Cambridge: Cambridge University Press.

Habitat for Humanity. 1993. Kenya Pilot Project: National Urban Data Collection and Dissemination. *Habitat News* 15(1) (April): 34–35.

Hankins, Mark. 1987. *Renewable Energy in Kenya*. Nairobi: Motif Creative Arts.

Harral, Clell G. 1988. *Road Deterioration in Developing Countries: Causes and Remedies*. Washington, D.C.: World Bank.

Hedlund, Hans. 1992. *Coffee, Co-operatives and Culture: An Anthropological Study of Coffee Co-operatives in Kenya*. Nairobi: Oxford University Press.

Hetherington, Penelope. 1993. Explaining the Crisis of Capitalism in Kenya. *African Affairs* 92: 89–103.

Heyer, Judith. 1990. *Kenya: Monitoring Living Conditions and Consumption Patterns*. Geneva: United Nations Research Institute for Social Development.

Hoorweg, Jan, and Rudo Niemeijer. 1991. *Intervention in Child Nutrition: Evaluation Studies in Kenya*. Nairobi: AMREF.

Isaacs, Glynn, and John W. K. Harris. 1978. The Fossil Hominids and an Introduction to their Context, Archaeology. Pp. 64–85 in *Koobi Fora Research Project, Vol. 1*, Richard Leakey and Maeve Leakey, eds. Oxford: Clarendon Press.

Johnson, Frederick. 1967. *A Standard Swahili-English Dictionary*. Oxford: Oxford University Press.

Kachru, Braj, ed. 1982. *The Other Tongue: English Across Cultures*. Oxford: Pergamon Press.

Kenya Pilot Project. 1993. Kenya Pilot Project: National Urban Data Collection and Dissemination. *Habitat News* 15(1) (April): 34–35.

Kenyatta, Jomo. 1938. *Facing Mount Kenya: The Traditional Life of the Gikuyu*. Nairobi: Heinemann Kenya, 1989.

Khamala, C. P. M., ed. 1980. *Science and Technology for Development: Proceedings of a Seminar of the Kenya National Academy for the Advancement of Arts and Sciences, March 1978*. Nairobi: Kenya National Academy for the Advancement of Arts and Sciences.

Khamala, C. P. M., and John B. Castelino, eds. 1979. *Energy Resources in East Africa: Proceedings of the 12th Annual Symposium of the East African Academy, August 1976*. Nairobi: Kenya National Academy for the Advancement of Arts and Sciences.

Khasiani, Shanyisa A., ed. 1992. *Groundwork: African Women as Environmental Managers*. Nairobi: ACTS Press.

King, Kenneth. 1977. *The African Artisan: Education and the Informal Sector in Kenya*. London: Macmillan.

Kitching, Gavin. 1980. *Class and Economic Change in Kenya: The Making of an African Petite Bourgeoise, 1905–1970*. New Haven: Yale University Press.

Koch, Gerd. 1986. *The Material Culture of Kiribati*. Guy Slatter, trans. Suva: University of the South Pacific.

Konvitz, Joseph W., Mark H. Rose, and Joel A. Parr. 1990. Technology and the City. *Technology and Culture* 31: 248–94.

Kumar, J. K. 1987. *Plantation Life in Kenya*. Nairobi: self-published.

Kyendo, Musyoka wa, and Njehu Gatabaki. 1992. The Kalenjin. *Finance* 31 July: 10–31.

Leakey, Louis. 1959. *First Lessons in Kikuyu*. Nairobi: Kenya Literature Bureau.

Lee-Smith, Diana, Mutsembi Manundu, Davinder Namra, and Kuria Gathuru. 1987. *Urban Food Production and the Cooking Fuel Situation in Urban Kenya*. Nairobi: Mazingira Institute. Summarized in Kenya: A Fuel Wood Case Study, *Urban Perspectives* 3(1) (November 1992): 16.

Leo, Christopher. 1984. *Land and Class in Kenya*. Toronto: University of Toronto Press.

Leone, Mark P. 1973. Archaeology as the Science of Technology. Pp. 125–50 in *Research and Theory in Current Archaeology*, Charles L. Redman, ed. New York: John Wiley and Sons.

Lipton, Michael, with Richard Longhurst. 1989. *New Seeds and Poor People*. London: Unwin Hyman.

Little, P. D. 1992. *The Elusive Granary: Herder, Farmer and State in Northern Kenya*. Cambridge: Cambridge University Press.

Mack, John. 1986. *Madagascar: Island of the Ancestors* London: The British Museum.

Martz, H. F., and W. J. Zimmer. 1992. The Risk of Catastrophic Failure of the Solid Rocket Boosters of the Space Shuttle. *American Statistician* 46(1) (February): 42–47.

Matson, A. T. 1972. *The Nandi Resistance to British Rule, 1890–1906*. Nairobi: East African Publishing House.

Maxwell, D., and S. Zziwa. 1992. *Urban Farming in Africa: The Case of Uganda*. Nairobi: ACTS Press.

Mayer, Philip, and Iona Mayer. 1961. *Townsmen or Tribesmen: Conservatism and the Process of Urbanization in a South African City*. Cape Town: Oxford University Press.

Mbaabu, Ireri. 1985. *New Horizons in Kiswahili: A Synthesis in Developments, Research and Literature*. Nairobi: Kenya Literature Bureau.

Mbwagwa, R. K. 1980. *Physical Development Plan for Eldoret, 1980–1985*. Eldoret: Ministry of Housing, Public Works and Physical Planning.

Meillassoux, Claude. 1981. *Maidens, Meal and Money: Capitalism and the Domestic Economy.* Cambridge: Cambridge University Press.

Moga, Jacko, and Dan Fee. 1993. *Sheng Dictionary.* Nairobi: Ginseng Press.

Morley, David, and Hermione Lovell. 1986. *My Name Is Today: An Illustrated Discussion of Child Health, Society, and Poverty in Less-Developed Countries.* London: Macmillan.

Niemcynowicz, Janusz. 1992. Water Drainage and Urban Development: A Call for Realistic Alternatives for the Future. *Impact of Science on Society* no. 166, 42(2): 131–47.

Nyaribo, F. B., and D. L. Young. 1992. Impacts of Capital and Land Constraints on the Economics of New Livestock Technology in Western Kenya. *Agricultural Economics* 6(4) (April): 353–64.

Ochieng', William R., ed. 1990. *Themes in Kenyan History.* Nairobi: Heinemann Kenya.

Odada, J. E. O., and A. B. Ayako, eds. 1989. *The Impact of Structural Adjustment Policies on the Wellbeing of the Vulnerable Groups in Kenya.* Nairobi: UNICEF and Kenyan Economic Association.

Odingo, Richard S. 1971. *The Kenya Highlands: Land Use and Agricultural Development.* Nairobi: East African Publishing House.

Ogutu, M. A. 1979. Agriculture and the Development of Markets in the Western Province of Kenya, 1930–1960. Pp. 216–42 in *Ecology and History in East Africa.* Nairobi: Kenya Literature Bureau.

Ojany, F. F., and R. B. Ogendo. 1973. *Kenya: A Study in Human Physical Geography.* Nairobi: Longman.

Olinde, Ken Nyando. 1986. *Sheng: An Investigation into the Social Structural Aspects of an Evolving Language.* B.A. Thesis, Department of English, Nairobi University.

Parkin, David, ed. 1975. *Town and Country in Central and Eastern Africa.* London: Oxford University Press and International African Institute.

Patel, I. B., Mangat and Partners. In association with Watson Hawksley. 1981. *Eldoret Water Resources Investigation Report.* Nairobi: Mangat and Partners.

Patel, N. M., and V. K. Vashista. 1992. *Standard Eight: Learning Science and Agriculture.* Nairobi: Malimu.

Petroski, Henry. 1985. *To Engineer is Human: The Role of Failure in Successful Design.* London: Macmillan.

Pugh, Cedric. 1992. Land Policies and Low-Income Housing in Developing Countries: A Review, with Reference to Kenya and India. *Land Use Policies* 9 (January): 47–63.

Pye, David. 1968. *The Nature and Art of Workmanship.* Cambridge: Cambridge University Press.

Rasmussen, Jens, Keith Duncan, and Jacques Leplat. 1987. *New Technology and Human Error.* Chichester: John Wiley.

Redclift, Michael. 1987. *Sustainable Development: Exploring the Contradictions.* London: Routledge.

Regis, Edward, ed. 1985. *Extraterrestrials: Science and Alien Intelligence.* Cambridge: Cambridge University Press.

Rosenberg, Nathan, and L. E. Birdzell. 1990. Science, Technology and the Western Miracle. *Scientific American* 263(5) (November): 18–25.

Smithsonian Institution. 1985. *Aditi: The Living Arts of India.* Washington, D.C.: Smithsonian Institution Press.

Smyth, Mary, ed. 1987. *Cognition in Action.* Hillsdale, N. J.: Lawrence Erlbaum.

Sodipo, J. Olubi. 1992. Philosophy and Scientific/Technological Development in Africa. Paper delivered at a departmental seminar, Department of Philosophy, Moi University, December 1, 1992.

Spencer, Paul. 1992. Re-enactment of the Tragedy of the Commons in Kenya [review of Little 1992]. *Current Anthropology* 33(4): 481–83.

Stichter, Sharon. 1982. *Migrant Labour in Kenya: Capitalism and African Response, 1895–1975.* London: Longman.

Stichter, Sharon, and Jane Parpart, eds. 1988. *Patriarchy and Class: African Women in the Home and the Workforce.* Boulder, Colo.: Westview Press.

Sutton, J. E. G. 1976. The Kalenjin. Pp. 21–52 in *Kenya Before 1900: Eight Regional Studies,* B. A. Ogot, ed. Nairobi: East African Publishing House.

Urevbu, Andrew O. 1991. Impact of Science and Technology on Everyday Life: An African Perspective. *Impact of Science on Society* No. 161, 41(3): 2–13.

Vansina, Jan. 1984. *Art History in Africa.* London: Longman.

Varcoe, Ian, ed. 1990. *Deciphering Science and Technology: The Social Relations of Expertise.* London: Macmillan.

Warren, Kay B., and Susan C. Bourque. 1989. Women, Technology, and Development Ideologies: Frameworks and Findings. Pp. 382–410 in *Gender and Anthropology: Critical Reviews for Research and Teaching,* Sandra Morgen, ed. Washington, D.C.: American Anthropological Association.

Whisnant, David E. 1986. *All that is Native and Fine: The Politics of Culture in an American Region.* Chapel Hill: University of North Carolina Press.

White, Landeg. 1987. *Magomero: Portrait of an African Village.* Cambridge: Cambridge University Press.

White, Luise. 1990. *The Comforts of Home: Prostitution in Colonial Nairobi.* Chicago: University of Chicago Press.

———. 1993. Cars Out of Place: Vampires, Technology and Labor in East and Central Africa. *Representations* 43 (summer): 27–50.

Whorf, Benjamin Lee. 1956. *Language, Thought and Reality: Selected Writings of Benjamin Lee Whorf.* Raymond Carroll, ed. Cambridge, Mass.: MIT Press.

Williams, Rosalind. 1990. *Notes on the Underground: An Essay on Technology, Society and the Imagination.* Cambridge, Mass.: MIT Press.

Wiredu, Kwasi. 1980. *Philosophy and an African Culture.* Cambridge: Cambridge University Press.

Wisner, Ben. 1989. *Power and Need in Africa.* Trenton, N.J.: Africa World Press.

World Health Organization. 1988. *Air Pollution in African Villages and Cities.* Geneva: World Health Organization.

Zeleza, Tiyambe. 1987. *Labour, Unionization and Women's Participation in Kenya.* Nairobi: Friedrich Ebert Foundation.

Zuidema, F. C., ed. 1987. *Manual of Drainage in Urban Areas,* 2 vols. Paris: UNESCO.

Index

accidents, motor vehicle, 77, 78, 115
"action," 23
advertising, in Kenya, 95, 178, 213
Agricultural Society of Kenya (ASK)
    Fair, 191, 197
agriculture, 49, 55, 193; produce,
    118
aluminum cans, 25
Arabic language, 175–76
archaeology, 150, 159
artisans, 60, 120, 123–24, 133, 138,
    178, 189, 195. *See also* fundi
Asian commerce, in Kenya, 90, 91,
    121, 125, 134–35, 163, 183, 192,
    193, 194–95
Asian food, 45
Asian transport, 65
Asians (people from the Indian
    subcontinent) in Eldoret, 28, 48, 52,
    80, 188; as managers, 127, 128, 131,
    200
askaris (security guards), 7, 29, 62, 87,
    149, 185, 196, 211
associations, commercial, 123–25
automobile: parts, 109, 111, 125–26,
    213; repair, 111, 137

balance: of bicycles, 63–65; in children,
    69–70, 71; and gender differences,
    69–70
ballpoint pens, 135–36
Barn'getuny Plaza, 128, 129–30, 169–
    70, 191
batteries, 83, 85
biashara (Swahili, "business")
    housing, 184–85
bicycles: loading, 63–64, 148–49;
    movement, 6, 66, 74; repair, 67;
    shops, 95; uses, 48, 63, 76
Biwott, Nicholas (Kalenjin politician),
    11, 61, 169
bottles: and caps, 151, 153; glass, 148–
    49, 195; plastic, 156
bricklayers, 128
Bukusu. *See* Luhya
bus transportation, 144

capitalization of technologies, 39, 56,
    80, 125, 128, 183, 191
carpenters, 121, 127
cash registers, 136
cassette players, tapes, 81–83, 85
Central Province, 61, 181

chameleons, 12

charcoal: as cleaning agent, 44; commercial production of, 34, 44, 48; consumption, 45; domestic production of, 34–37; as heat source, 33, 37, 43; *makaa* (Swahili), 33, 212; transport, 64

chickens: commercial production of, 65–66, 195; transport of, 66, 76

China, People's Republic of: and aid to Kenya, 130; and commerce with Kenya, 92

chungu (Swahili, "earthenware pot"), 40

circumcision, 146–47

cities, attitudes toward, 59–60

clothes, second-hand (*mitumba*), 84, 95, 190, 193

Coca-Cola, 148, 177

colonialism, 59, 183

combine (agricultural machine), 49, 54, 58

commerce, Kenyan, 90, 91

communication: cross-cultural, 142–43; in pastoral settings, 115, 213

competition, 120, 133

computers, 203

construction, 126–27, 154, 170, 191–92

copying (xerography), 111–12

cows: as meat source, 44; and urban grazing, 3, 157

crowds, urban, 73, 74

decision models, 135, 137, 138, 142, 145–46, 149

design, in history of technology, 143

disabilities, physical, 70–72, 199

district commissioner's residence, 10

dollmaker, 112, 152

donkeys, 114, 119

DP (Democratic Party), 185

drainage channels, 9, 149, 157–58, 161–62, 166

drivers: bus, 144; matatu, 76–77, 146; truck, 117

earnings, of laborers, 15, 30, 41, 67, 81, 182

EATEC (East African Tannin Extract Company), xii, 34, 48, 138, 148, 211

ecology, 2, 12, 15, 25, 86

education, 56; technical, 95–96

Eldo Center (shopping center), 127, 130

Eldoret: climate, 37; commerce, 91, 107; industries, 99 (*see also* KCC, Ken-Knit, Raiply); layout, 4–6, 72, 80, 93, 121, 151; location, xi; maps, 209–10; origin of name, 164–65; periurban settlements (Langas and Huruma), 21, 53, 189, 211–12; population, 50

Eldoret Club, 13, 29, 46, 87

Eldoret Municipal Council, 189, 192, 194

electricity: fixtures for, 92; as heat source, 33, 39, 40, 43; distribution of, 80, 87, 88; metering of, 88; supply of, 79

Elligirini-Endoroto Rivers, 160

engineering, hydrological, 163

English language, 28, 97, 174–75, 177, 212

error structure, 137–38
Europeans, 141–42; as managers, 127
Eveready batteries, 20
experts, 94, 112

filmmaking, 85
FORD (Forum of Rural Democracy
    party), 185, 197
French language, 175
functionalism, 200–201
fundi (Swahili, "artisan"), 94, 99–100,
    212–13; materials, 109; regulation
    of, 113; types of, 94–95, 120, 183
furniture, 64, 68, 121, 155
gardening, 15, 27–28, 31–32, 35, 48
GEPS (General Electrical Products
    Supply), 91, 97
glass, 159
golf course, 29
graffiti, 184–85
grasses, 156–57

hairdressing (*kinyozi*), 61–62, 131,
    180; signs, 177, 181
hawkers, 81–82, 120, 123–24, 188,
    189, 195, 197
Hindus, 93; temples, 152, 177, 186–87.
    See also Asians

ibis, hadada, 12
industry, in Kenya, 63, 83
informal sector, 133, 190–91
irio (Kikuyu, "vegetable stew"), 41

jembe (Swahili, "shovel"), 27, 159,
    168
jiko (Swahili, "stove" or "kitchen"),

37–38, 39, 41; fabrication of, 108–9,
    155
jua kali (artisan area, from Swahili,
    "fierce sun"), 44, 120–21, 123, 133,
    197

K Square (Eldoret suburb), 190
Kakamega (western Kenya town), 27,
    56, 89, 123
Kalenjin, 14, 48, 189, 192, 193; Elgeyo
    (subgroup), 57; food, 44; identity,
    50, 89; Nandi (subgroup), 51;
    Sabaot (subgroup), 51; Tugen
    (subgroup), 50, 89
Kalenjin language, 165, 174, 175
KANU (Kenya All National Union
    party), 57, 84, 185, 191, 192
Kapsabet (Rift Valley town), 61
Kapsoya (section of Eldoret), 1, 2, 160
Karandusi (Rift Valley Paleolithic
    site), 155–56
KCC (Kenya Cooperative Creameries),
    2
Ken-Knit (textile factory), 4, 9, 11
Kenya National Examinations
    Council, 96
Kenyan National Academy for the
    Advancement of Arts and Sciences,
    138
Kenyan Post and Telecommunications
    Company (KPTC), 141
Kenyan Power and Lighting Company
    (KPLC), 87, 88
Kenyatta, Jomo (first president of
    independent Kenya), 36–37, 75,
    182
keys, metal, 101–3

Kikuyu, 27, 31, 46, 50, 61, 62, 190,
192; food, 41; language, 35, 71;
technology, 36–37, 106, 181
kilns, for charcoal making, 35–37, 48
Kisumu (city on Lake Victoria), 52,
159; market, 118; National
Museum, 24
Kitale (city north of Eldoret), 51
KVDA (Kerio Valley Development
Authority), 79, 169

labor transfers, 56
land clashes, 50–51, 196
law, in Kenya, 91
locksmiths, 101–3, 112, 197, 198
Luhya: Bukusu (subgroup), 14, 51, 54,
61, 211; food, 41; language, 174;
Maragoli (subgroup), 51
Luo, 146, 185

Maasai, 51, 164–65
mail delivery, 101–2
maize: cultivation of, 55; dehulling
machinery, 147; roasted, 41–42,
151, 155; storage, 118
"majimboism" (political doctrine), 52
management, 126, 130; and division of
labor, 131
manyanga (Sheng, "minivan"), 84
market: in central Eldoret, 101, 118,
120, 123, 190, 193; informal, 190,
192, 198
masons, 126, 127
mass movement, rhythms of, 6
matatu (mass transit), 4, 40–41, 51,
56, 75–77, 84, 114, 138, 189, 198;
origin of name, 75

men: economic roles of, 49, 52, 59, 60,
68–69, 76, 97, 119; identity of, 19,
101, 149, 200; training of, 67, 113
Mickey Mouse, 186
"middleman minority," 92–93
migrants, into Eldoret, 31–32, 36, 43–
44, 49–50, 134
milk, 1–2, 58, 153; fermented, 44
"mob justice," 73–74
Moi, Daniel arap (second president of
Kenya), 50, 182
Moi Avenue, 93, 152, 177, 186
Moi University, 39, 57, 130
moles (rodents), 15, 27, 31
Mombasa (port city), 193
mursik (Kalenjin, "fermented cow's
milk"), 44
mzungu. See wazungu

Nairobi (capital of Kenya), 52, 78, 79,
87, 123, 124, 171, 196–97
Nairobi National Museum, 24
Nairobi Road, 3, 4, 6, 7, 10, 11, 118,
138, 178
Nakuru (Rift Valley city), 20, 59, 124,
173
Nandi Road, 6, 8, 10, 13–14, 15, 16,
130, 167
Nation (newspaper), 52, 96, 123, 135,
190, 197
newspapers, 188
numeracy/innumeracy, 128, 136
nut cones, paper, 153, 202–3
nyama choma (Swahili, "roasted
meat"), 44
Nyerere, Julius (former president of
Tanzania), 94

oil filters, automotive, 20, 25, 166
oil pipeline, 59, 173

panga (long, broad-bladed knife), 47
paper, 151, 153
paraffin (kerosene), 39, 43, 45, 153
"part" appreciation, 104–5, 108
photography, 182–83, 205–7; on signs, 178, 182
plastic bags, 153, 195
poetics of technology, definition, xi, 176
poles, installation of, for electricity, xii–xiii
politics: campaigns, 177, 182; issues, 85, 123, 133, 189–90
pornography, 84
post office, 161
potatoes, 119–20
power rationing, 80
power tools, 121, 122

radio broadcasts, 84
radioactivity, 135, 149
railroad, 171, 173
Raiply (plywood plant), 152
recycling, 20, 109
"red mercury," 134–35
restaurants, 45
Rift Valley (Province), 50, 51
road construction, 167, 168
road crews: power company, 88–89; telephone, 175
Roman alphabet, 177, 178
Roman Catholic cathedral, 186
rubber stamps, 105–6
rubber strips, 18, 20, 25, 152

rungu (Swahili, "knobbed staff of chiefly office"), 19
running, 212

Safari Rally (annual car race), 23
scavengers, 25, 132, 153–54
security bars, 107–8
sewage plant, 161, 165
sewing machines, 98–99
shamba (Swahili, "farmstead"), 1, 55, 60
Sheng (new Kenyan language), 77, 84, 212
shilling, Kenyan, 81
shoemakers, 71, 94–95, 110, 112, 113, 152
shops: demolition of, 124, 190–91; machine, 121; organization of, 123, 131, 194
signs, 111, 177–82; painting of, 178, 180–81
Sikhs, 93, 127, 157, 188
Sirikwa Hotel, 169
snares (animal traps), 29, 31–32
social stratification, 39–40, 60, 80, 85, 113
Sodipo, J. Olubi (Nigerian philosopher), 137, 138
solidarity, organic and mechanical, 116–17
Sosia River, 2, 156, 159, 160, 164–65, 197
South Africans, 50, 195
space shuttle Challenger, 144
State Lodge (president's official residence), 10–11, 14, 46, 142
sticks, 19

sukumu wiki (Swahili, "get through the week"; also a type of leaf green), 40–41
supermarkets, 194–95
supervision, 117, 127, 142
suspension, automobile. See wheeled toys
Swahili language (Kiswahili), 73, 77, 174–75, 176, 177

tailors, 95, 97, 106, 111, 112, 113
tallying practice, 136
Tana River, 79
teamwork, 113, 116, 117, 118, 121–22, 125, 128
telephone repair crews, 140–41, 142
terminology, technical, 67
Timboroa (town south of Eldoret), 57, 119, 165
tires, automobile, 18–19, 73, 110, 190
torches, welding, 106–7
touts (manamba), 75–76, 77, 84–85
tractors, 2, 49, 53
traffic, vehicular, 171–72
training, technical, 96, 97, 105, 143
transformers, step-down, 80, 91
trap maker, 112
trash: collection, 25, 131–32; surface accumulation of, 150
trees: and clearing techniques, 47; for charcoal making, 35, 45–46; and lumber supply, 121
truck ("lorry"): breakdown, 15–16, 115–16; uses of, 58

Turkanas, 3, 23, 50, 211
Turkwel River, 79

Uasin Gishu (District), 49
Uganda, 2, 79
underground pipes, 27, 160

videos: and exhibition parlors, 85–86

Wajir (town in far north Kenya), 135
walking, 70, 72
water: control strategies, 168–69; flow, 155, 164, 167–68, 169–70; pipes, 160, 167; and politics, 164; sources, 48
wazungu (Swahili, "foreigners"; singular, mzungu), 1, 12, 41, 211
Webuye (town north of Eldoret), 54
Weekly News (short-lived Eldoret newspaper), 143, 203
welders, 106–8, 111, 143
wheat, 61
wheelchairs, 70, 71–72
wheeled toys: comparison of, 18, 24; construction of, 17–18, 20–24, 156; "Mercedes," 19–20; motion of, 8–9; "Peugeot," 23
Whorf, Benjamin Lee, 144
wire, 21
Wiredu, Kwasi (Ghanaian philosopher), 137
witchcraft, 147
women: economic roles of, 52–53, 57, 58–59, 68–69, 76, 97–98, 112, 119–20, 131, 193; life stories of, 53–62; and technology, 54; training of, 67–68

About the Author

RICHARD M. SWIDERSKI lived in the Kenyan highland town of Eldoret for two years while teaching anthropology at Moi University, some thirty-five kilometers away by daily bus.

Swiderski, who has a Ph.D. in cultural anthropology from Princeton, an M.A. in TESOL (Teaching English to Speakers of Other Languages) from the School of International Training, and a B.A. in Romance languages from Johns Hopkins, has previously taught anthropology and conducted research in the United States, India, East Asia, and the Near East.

Swiderski is the author of several books and numerous articles. His current research concentrates on technologies of infectious-disease monitoring and international response.